# The Third Revolution

A Study of Psychiatry
& Religion by

## KARL STERN

London
MICHAEL JOSEPH

*First published by*
MICHAEL JOSEPH LTD
*26 Bloomsbury Street*
*London, W.C.*1
1955

*Set and printed in Great Britain by Tonbridge Printers Ltd,*
*Peach Hall Works, Tonbridge, Kent, in Times eleven on*
*thirteen point, on an antique wove paper made by Henry Bruce*
*at Currie in Scotland, and bound by James Burn at Esher*

H3

157-

4/6.

# THE THIRD REVOLUTION

Also by Karl Stern

THE PILLAR OF FIRE

To
MY WIFE

*Nihil obstat:*  Delphis Rollin, ptre.
            Ottawa, le 12 mars 1954

*Imprimatur:* ✠ M. J. Lemieux, o.p.
            Archbishop of Ottawa
            Ottawa, le 15 mars 1954

Some of the ideas presented here are enlargements on observations which the author has published in essays here and there. Occasionally sentences and paragraphs are repeated from these earlier essays, without special acknowledgement. In this study, various trends in the history of psychiatry are outlined in their fundamental features but not more than is necessary for the presentation of the argument. Anyone who wants to obtain a fuller view of the subject has to consult technical books. Many cases had to be described in episodic form; interpretations given here are frequently based on a greater amount of material than is actually presented. Wherever case histories are mentioned they are taken from actual experience but, in accord with common usage in medical books, external details are changed in such a way that the identity of the patient is completely unrecognizable.

As happens so often with studies of this kind, many ideas have developed out of collaboration and discussion with friends, especially Dr Victorin Voyer. Particular acknowledgements go to Rev. Father François M. Drouin, O.P., Fr Richard Mignault, O.P., and Fr Henri Gratton, O.M.I., for the critical appraisal of this study. I also wish to thank Miss Cecilia McGuire for her patient help in the preparation of the manuscript.

K. S.

# CONTENTS

# I         The Controversy

*What thought can think, another thought can mend.*
ROBERT SOUTHWELL, *Look Home*

WHEN I was a medical student, we used to have one or two lectures on psychiatry each week. Psychiatry was a purely medical subject, and I remember that in our weekly schedule it was sandwiched in between 'Ear, Nose, and Throat' (from nine to ten) and 'Surgery' (from eleven to twelve). Strictly speaking, the subject was called 'Psychiatry and Neurology,' and our lectures were mostly given by a white-haired *Geheimrat* who had earned his academic chair by a famous paper on 'Hemichorea associated with a lesion of the superior cerebellar peduncle' (which can be translated as Saint Vitus's Dance on one side of the body caused by damage to a certain part of the brain). Just as 'Ear, Nose, and Throat' were all three the domain of one professor, so were neurology and psychiatry.

These lectures were given in a huge, dome-shaped amphitheatre, and included, like all other clinical lectures, a demonstration of patients. The *Geheimrat* talked for half an hour about a disease in a purely theoretical fashion (symptoms, course, diagnosis, prognosis, treatment). Then the door on his right would open and a patient would be

13

brought in, accompanied by a nurse and an assistant. The
lectures were invariably boring until the appearance of the
patient. There was always a moment of suspense before
that door opened because, unless the lecture was about
neurology, the patient would be an insane person, and
everybody knows the weird experience of being confronted
with a lunatic.

We would already have heard the details of the life
history of some Berlin *Hausfrau,* say an official's or a
merchant's wife. Then the door would open and we would
be confronted with a woman in blue hospital garb. (Why
the 'Neurology and Psychiatry' costumes were blue in many
hospitals I have never known.) Her hair was usually done
up in hanging braids, and she would either be crouched
and motionless, or would enter stamping, hitting, and
screaming invective, or she would instantly make for one
of the students and try to sit in his lap.

This was drama, and the weird effect was emphasized by
the fact that the *Geheimrat* was calm and detached, talked
to the patient in a friendly, human way, and by the closely-
knit and carefully-prepared scientific references he presented. Since the references (symptoms, course, diagnosis,
prognosis, and treatment) were framed in exactly the same
way as those used in 'Ear, Nose, and Throat' and 'Surgery,' we did not feel that there was anything about
psychiatry which would make it essentially different from
any other medical subject. If anyone had cornered us in
those days and asked us the question: 'What about religion
and psychiatry?' I am sure we would not have known what
he was talking about. It would have sounded just as
rational as a question about religion and pediatrics—that
is to say, not rational at all.

Those people in blue led in through the door on the

right who were not insane were neurological patients (persons suffering from tumours of the brain, or softening of the spinal cord, or degeneration of nerve pathways, or other maladies of the nervous system). In all such cases one can apply methods of thought and investigation resembling those which one applies when dealing with a broken leg or typhoid fever. In cases of insanity one can do so legitimately only up to a certain point. In the universities in which I studied, we were taught very little about a chapter of psychiatry which is commonly presented under the heading of 'Neuroses.'

Now there are living in our midst thousands and thousands of people (there is a strong possibility that they form the majority of mankind in our present civilization) who suffer, or produce suffering among those around them, in a most puzzling manner. They live in mortal anxiety, or they are unable to hope, or they are entangled in mysterious hatred, they are out to destroy that which would give them happiness, they are incapable of trusting, or they are being oppressed by something which is best called insatiable remorse. They form a huge army of suffering, dissatisfaction, frustration, and assault. They are not in blue uniforms like those patients who came through the door on the right; they are not distinguished in that way from the mass of people around us.

While I use the metaphor of a huge army, I realize that it is not quite justified. Instead of the solidarity of an army, there is an element of self-isolation in each of these cases, and the entire phenomenon is so amorphous that at first glance it seems to resist any systematic attempt at clarification. This may be one of the reasons why our *Geheimrat* spoke so little of such things; 'symptoms, diagnosis, course, prognosis, and treatment' were no longer applicable. If an observer could, at one glance, behold all the neurotic suffering and entanglement in the world today, and could look into the hearts of these unhappy people, he would get the impression of something quite infernal.

Infernal is a good word for it. Many of our neurotic patients express the thought literally: 'This is hell on earth.' Those around them often say: 'Life with that person is like hell on earth.' The mystics state that hell is a perpetual state of inability to love. Berdyaev once made a remarkable comparison between Dante and Dostoievsky. He said that Dante represented the world image of Medieval Man for whom heaven, hell, and purgatory were something like neat topographic entities. Dostoievsky, says Berdyaev, speaks for modern man in a manner analogous to that of Dante; but the drama of Dostoievsky's man is such that each individual life is a Dantesque microcosmos, mysteriously penetrated by *all three worlds*. The three worlds are no longer merely three neat circles, mapped out in geometrical fashion, but all of us—the Raskolnikovs and Stavrogins, the Alyoshas and Myshkins—carry in our souls very real elements of a Dantesque cosmos, with eternal potentialities.

The world of neurosis is one which cannot be easily sandwiched in between 'Ear, Nose, and Throat' on one hand and 'Surgery' on the other. Concepts arise which seem strangely unrelated to the curriculum of the medical student, concepts such as Love and Hatred, Fear and Hope, Guilt and Freedom. These are concepts which have figured for many centuries in the vocabulary of philosophers and theologians. Now, as if from nowhere, they suddenly turn up in the dictionary of clinicians.

Thus we are, in the present study, entering a borderland in which there seems to exist a state of confusion. Those who have already been there for ages, the philosophers and theologians, do not want to give up their domain to recent intruders. The intruders, on the other hand, feel that the ancient occupants had no claim to it in the first place. Some representatives of both sides feel that a *modus vivendi* can be found by which the area could be settled jointly.

Today, the controversy concerning 'psychiatry and religion' is as widespread as was the one concerning biology and religion in our grandfather's time, and probably even more heated. It is presently being discussed in technical books and journals, in popular lectures and magazines. It forms the subject of novels and plays. Hardly a day passes that I am not approached on the subject, by physicians, medical students, nurses, ministers, and priests. Many of these people speak of it as if it represented a troubling personal problem. I am also asked to deal with the question in lectures and before discussion groups of various kinds, Catholic and Protestant alike. There is no doubt that all this began with the advent of psycho-analysis, and that without psycho-analysis it would never have come about. Nevertheless, psycho-analysis is by no means the only starting-point.

For instance, some years ago a professor of philosophy, an expert on Plato and Kierkegaard, told me about an incident that occurred during one of his lectures on ethics. His students had produced an illustrated magazine, containing an article reporting that a person's moral principles depend on the function of the frontal lobes of the brain. When parts of the frontal lobes are removed, all moral restraints are apt to go. The students felt that morality must therefore be a matter of biological evolution, animal training, and so on. In other words, morality depends on the function of colloidal substance in the same way that

sugar metabolism depends on the pancreas. It is obvious
that this argument is completely opposed to the Christian
idea of morality. However, it has nothing to do with psycho-
analysis and it refers to the branch of science known as the
physiology of the brain.

Similarly, students often approach me regarding what
they consider the doubtful metaphysical nature and abso-
luteness of morality. But they use a different argument.
They point out that social *mores* are determined by cultural
and biological conditions: though to us killing is sinful,
the Eskimos let their old people die from exposure (I have
never been able to determine whether this is true) and
regard it as right. Since concepts of right and wrong are
thus determined by custom, they say, it is sheer superstition
to believe that they are of supernatural origin. Again this
argument has nothing to do with psycho-analysis. It forms
part of a widely accepted philosophy, prevalent among
many cultural anthropologists and social psychologists,
called cultural relativism. However, both arguments have
in common the premise that morality cannot possibly be
anchored in a metaphysical space; it is a product of, and
conditioned by, elements of the material order, such as
brain cells or geographical conditions.

Nevertheless, psycho-analysis itself still represents the
biggest challenge to religious values. Just as the nineteenth-
century controversy between biology and religion would
never have started without Darwin, the present-day controversy between psychiatry and religion would never have
started without Freud. Today Darwin's theory of evolution does not seem to have as much bearing on Christianity
as people thought fifty years ago. With psycho-analysis,
however, it is quite different. To the uninitiated, Freud's
papers on psychology read for the most part like straight

pornography, his pamphlets on religion represent sheer
atheism. All this, the believing man thinks, cannot help
having a negative effect on Christianity. On the other hand,
it is confusing to learn that some serious religious thinkers,
Catholic as well as Protestant, uphold psycho-analysis as a
theory and as a tool of treatment, and that in the Soviet
Union, where atheistic materialism is the state doctrine,
psycho-analysis is banned. This is typical of our time. All
things seem to be complex and elusive.

However, this puts an even greater obligation on us. We
cannot afford to stand by and wait for things to sort themselves out. The better one becomes acquainted with the
psycho-analytic movement, the more one realizes that it
represents the opening of a new era no less significant than
the Galilean era in physics. Our image of the 'interior
world' will never be the same as it was before the year
1894. The scope of this change will be perceptible only
much later, in its historical perspective.

Moreover, we are—particularly in America—in the
midst of a tremendous development in all the psychological and social sciences, one of such dimensions and
potentialities that it would be no exaggeration to call it
a 'revolution.' Let us, for the want of a better term, call it
the Comtean revolution. Auguste Comte, the nineteenth-
century philosopher, dreamed of a world in which revelation and faith would be entirely supplanted by science.
Science in this case means first the science of man, that is,
psychology and sociology.

Is it possible that we are entering the age of Comte without realizing it? In the pages that follow a lot will be said
to justify such an apprehension. Although the outward
appearances are much less dramatic, the dehumanizing and
destructive forces inherent in this development are no less

formidable than they were in the case of the other two revolutions which arose out of the nineteenth century, the Marxist and the racist ones. This is an extreme comparison, but, as far as moral nihilism is concerned, the 'third' revolution has full potentialities of matching the other two.

Nevertheless, buried in it are also the most precious, creative currents. There are many reasons why we as Christians cannot afford to ignore this revolution. The situation is in a way similar to the one which presented itself in the thirteenth century: there exist outside the Christian sphere vast continents of thought which wait to be integrated. Since the beginning of modern times, the area of the gospel has been a frontier area. The Christian life is a life of challenge and response, even in the world of ideas.

In the face of these developments, a defensive attitude on the part of Christians becomes destructive. The temptation to ward off or shut out the seemingly alien is a sign of sterility. He who has the truth and does nothing but hoard it finds himself in the role of the debtor who buried his talent. If our lives are guided by fear of error, rather than the love of truth, we are no better than those people whose lives are dominated by a fear of sin rather than the love of good.

This is a time when, in the world of ideas, we need the spirit of courage and discernment which characterized people like Saint Thomas Aquinas. Saint Thomas, who was concerned with one aspect of the unity of truth, namely the integration of philosophical thought, had no need to bother with the integration of scientific discovery or with the relation between science and value. The sociologist, Georg Simmel, has remarked that all science has its natural limits; *whenever any particular branch of science attempts to give answers of universal validity, answers on ultimate questions concerning Man and the Universe, it oversteps its borders and goes wrong.* This thought was already implicit in Greek philosophy. What makes it so important for us today is the fact that secularism has created a philosophical vacuum in which science automatically expands. It is one of the aims of this book to rediscover the true borders of various sciences. Blurred demarcation lines have to be retraced. Therefore in the following chapters scientific discoveries will have to be discussed side by side with the philosophy of the discoverers. The former are admirable, and the latter are frequently questionable and flimsy. If this side-by-side consideration at times gives the impression that the present study is founded on an anti-scientific bias, it is erroneous.

There is a second reason for the necessity of a study such as this. The world is full of mental anguish. Our mental hospitals cannot cope with the number of patients who seek admittance. Alcohol and drug addiction are on the increase; so is the number of broken marriages. All these are signs that men are torn by irrational fear and hatred. Now just as psychologists and sociologists exhibit a bold belief in a scientific cure-all for these conditions— a naïve 'optimism of the technique'—the religious person is inclined to the opposite error, a naïve simplification by which faith loses its heroic quality and becomes a patent formula.

Modern man is stranded, but the preachers of the gospel are in danger of developing an 'I-told-you-so-if-you-only-had-followed-me' attitude. In practice this frequently leads to the situation that believers, the priests and levites of the parable, pass by while Modern Man, beaten and helpless in the ditch, has his wounds attended to by some other fellow. A purely negative attitude has had, as many Christian writers have pointed out, a devastating effect in the early phases of the social revolution in the last century; Pope Pius XI made the famous remark that the tragedy of the nineteenth century was that the Church lost the working-classes. Let us hope that in the future it will not be noted as a tragedy of the twentieth century that we have been standing by while a most important phase was being fought in the struggle for the human soul.

# II
# The Case of the Old Immigrant

*Portions and parcels of the dreadful past.*
TENNYSON, *The Lotos-Eaters*

IN those amphitheatre lectures in my medical-student days, the boundaries of the world of insanity seemed clearly determined. The people who came through the ominous door were as different from us, the students in the audience, as an abscessed thigh is different from a healthy thigh. The borders of the world of neurosis, however, are blurred and not quite perceptible. The existentialist philosophers tell us—and they tell us nothing new—that despair and anxiety, hatred and distrust lurk in a potential pit which surrounds us all, no matter how healthy we think we are.

There are people today who think, for reasons which we shall understand better at a later point, that the distinction between 'psychosis' and 'neurosis' does not hold any more. However, every lay person knows that most people who are confined to our state hospitals are sicker than those around us who are subject to what is commonly called morbid anxiety. This implies something of which we are certain—namely, that there are degrees of severity in psychological disturbances.

23

We may ask ourselves: what really constitutes a *degree* of severity in psychological disorders? The question is best answered by examples, and in citing them let us assume an important fictitious premise—that you have known the following three persons very well for a long time, as well as one knows one's best friends.

You meet the first friend and he has an expression of sadness: he looks as if he had just been crying. You find out that for three days he has hardly eaten or slept, and he seems to have lost all interest in his usual activities, either work or recreation. On enquiring you find out that three days ago, through an unfortunate accident, he lost a close and beloved relative. In other words, he is in a state of grief and mourning. This is a depressive state, to be sure, but by our common standards it is 'quite normal.' It would not be quite normal if your friend ignored his bereavement and had no reaction whatsoever. In that case, you would rightly think that there must be something 'wrong with him.' From the point of view of the preservation of life and of social conduct, it is 'abnormal' to eat too little, to sleep too little, and to show no interest in work or recreation. Similarly, if your friend's state lasted too long, it would constitute a true illness. Without going into the philosophy of illness, we can say that symptoms of grief and mourning represent a strange duality familiar to the physiology and pathology of the body: something which is against the intrinsic laws of life (not eating, not sleeping, complete lack of interest) is, in a given situation and to a certain degree, normal and seems even to fulfil a healthy purpose. In fact, were symptoms of grief completely absent, serious disturbances might be expected at a later stage in life.

Consider, however, the following case. You meet a

second friend whom you have known all your life. You are driving a car and you offer him a lift. He declines and you urge him. Finally he confides to you, quite bashfully and with all the obvious signs of embarrassment, that he now has great difficulty getting into any closed vehicle. He says he would rather walk than become panicky inside a bus or automobile. He also suffers from tenseness and choking sensations on meeting people. He used to have these latter feelings on occasion before, almost ever since he remembers, but they have recently become worse. He knows that all this is 'crazy,' because he used to enjoy riding. He himself thinks that the whole thing goes back to his battle experiences in northern France. Ever since he had the horrifying experience of having been cut off from his unit for twenty-four hours, he has not been the same.

The third friend is one whom you have not seen for some time. Suddenly you receive a letter in which he says: 'For personal and humanitarian reasons, I have passed exams which are based on liberty. God helps those on whom descension has not come through transmogrification?' When you meet him you notice that his face seems to have changed. He looks harassed. He tells you that this very morning he detected an almost imperceptible cloud of dust which flew into his room through the fireplace. This was a sign of warning. The entire thing is 'mixed up with the white slave traffic.' He hears voices which tell him those things. An experience like the third encounter is extremely startling. One of the things which make it so startling is the fact that you feel as if your friend were 'no longer the same person.'

Now this leads us to an important observation. If we ask ourselves what actually makes the third case appear 'more severe' than the second one, the immediate, spontaneous answer is not based on practical considerations; it is not that the third person seems in danger of harming himself or other people; or that he seems to be less well equipped, through the function of rational judgment, to handle the practical exigencies of everyday routine. This impression of 'severity' is a simple primary experience, an experience which you do not need to analyse in its components. There is in the third case an element of tragic *otherness*, of mysterious estrangement. Everyday language always indicates best such primary qualities of experience: in French the word for insane is *aliéné*. One feels that the man in the second case (who, in traditional terminology, is called 'neurotic') is somehow less strange. There are, in the psychic life, degrees of immediate familiarity. If a hierarchy of deviation from the norm seems to exist, it is actually in terms of that 'familiarity of experience.'

If one studies the involved controversy which at one time in psychiatric literature arose around the distinction between 'neurosis' and 'psychosis,' and analyses scientific justifications for such a distinction, one can discern the following trends. In a psychotic person a 'larger part' of the 'total personality' is affected than in a neurotic person. In a psychotic person, the core of the personality is changed; neurosis affects a more peripheral part. In psychoses the contact with reality is more disturbed than in neuroses. As far as the *observer* (you in meeting your three friends) is concerned, the so-called function of empathy is maintained to a higher degree in the case of a neurotic than in the case of a psychotic patient.

What is meant by this last statement? By *empathy* is meant the function by which one re-feels another person's feelings, or re-experiences his experiences; it is the well-known function of 'putting oneself into another person's place.' What enables us to 'understand' the first case—the mourner—so much more immediately than the last example —the psychotic? It is an element of immediate understandability, and that element has two components.

One is empirical: we know *from experience* that people have certain facial expressions after certain things have happened to them. This has nothing to do with empathy. It is the same as the knowledge which we gather from inanimate nature; it is acquired in the same way as the knowledge that water begins to bubble after having been heated to a certain point. The second component is this: when you listen to the story of your friend's bereavement, you understand his reaction *as if you were he*. Even at this point attention should be drawn to a remarkable inner relationship. The three ways in which the severity of psychic disorder were characterized—the degree to which the total personality is affected, the degree to which the person has lost contact with reality, and the degree to which we perceive his plight with immediate empathic understanding— are actually related to one another. The fact that our third friend is no longer the person we have known; the fact that he does not share reality with us in the way in which one breathes the same atmosphere—what else does this convey except that we are no longer able to be with him in the same immediate manner in which we are with the mourner?

Those with clinical experience might doubt this statement. They might maintain that they are able to re-experience the experience of the third man, the psychotic patient, with the same ease as those of the preceding two. However, our clinician is probably confusing two mechanisms which are related to one another but which are not quite the same— the mechanism of interpretation and the mechanism of empathy. What we are discussing here is simple and naïve co-experience, something which all human beings have and which one cannot reduce to any technical components. But it is not quite the same thing as sympathy and pity. You might have more sympathy (meaning pity) for the insane person than for the first two. However, this does not imply that you are really able to put yourself into his place.

Let us now consider a fourth example. Towards the end of the Second World War, we had a patient in a medical ward —a woman in her thirties, pale, sick-looking, apparently underweight, who lay in bed, motionless, staring into space. She had been entirely mute for twenty-four hours, refusing to eat and completely sleepless for several days. The physician who had been treating her gave her history. She was married, had four children, and her husband had been overseas in active combat for four years. She had been told that he was due to have his first furlough in Canada, but, two weeks before his arrival, she received a cable that he had been killed in action. After this, she slowed down in all her actions, became unable to eat or sleep, and she had ideas that there was a weird plot going on in downtown Montreal, a plot of mysterious intrigues and machinations aimed at her life. She also heard voices accusing her and threatening her.

This woman suffered from what, in psychiatric terminology, is called a reactive depression, or to be still more specific, an abnormal grief reaction. Now if we try to apply to her the criteria mentioned above, the test of 'put yourself in her place,' we observe the following. A good many of her reactions are immediately understandable. If one had had her experience, one would also be sad, retarded in one's actions, and unable to eat or sleep. The expression 'abnormal grief reaction' seems paradoxical because in such a case it is normal, as we have already seen, to experience grief with all its psychological and physiological concomitants. Moreover, if she suffers from what seems a quantitative exaggeration of normal mourning, we remember immediately that the motive, in her case, is also of abnormal magnitude. Hers is not just a common story of bereavement; the circumstances of her blow are extraordinary, and you immediately 'feel with her' and concede that you, too, might be 'bowled over' to the same degree as she. If she had passed through her terrible experience without any perceptible reaction, the psychology of common sense would regard her behaviour as abnormal, and rightly so, because it is 'normal' to go through a reaction of grief. In other words, what makes our patient a clinical problem at all is not the reaction of sadness by itself but the *degree* of that reaction. For those who are interested in the philosophy of sickness in general, it is interesting in this connection that there are also in the field of physical illnesses reactions which are, in themselves, physiological but abnormal *only in degree*. In her case the reaction has assumed such proportions that her life might be endangered if no help were given to her.

Now let us regard another component of her illness, the experience of the mysterious plot, the voices, etc. It is obvious to everybody that these elements no longer constitute a quantitative exaggeration of grief. This is not, even in an exaggerated form, the normal experience one has at the loss of a beloved person. If you try the 'put-yourself-into' test, the symptoms do not immediately 'belong.' You might perhaps say: 'If I were in her shoes, I might also have gone mad,' but the content of her madness is *qualitatively* different from what is known to be normal in the reaction of mourning.

Here we have to anticipate something which will become clearer in later parts of this study: a distinction between the traditional psychiatry of the medical schools on one hand, and psycho-analysis on the other. Classical psychiatry, before the advent of psycho-analysis or in complete disregard of it, would have had the following scientific theory. It is known from the relation of cause and effect in the field of physical illness that a uniformity of causes may have varying effects. For every housemaid who develops a skin rash by using a certain metal polish, one can show nine others who use the same polish without developing any rash. For every nurse exposed to tubercle bacilli who develops severe pulmonary tuberculosis, one can show nine others who develop pulmonary tuberculosis either not at all or to a much lesser degree. And for every woman who after bereavement becomes insane, like our patient, one can show nine who remain normal. Traditional psychiatry would state that there was present in our patient, in a latent form, a predisposition towards a derangement of the function of the brain which is associated with delusions (bizarre erroneous ideas) and hallucinations (false sensory perceptions). The emotional blow, or perhaps the physical debility following it, acted as a trigger mechanism to set a mental breakdown in action for which she already had the potentiality fully present in her character.

The psycho-analyst, however, would say: if we know this woman's entire past, back to the earliest phases of her life, and provided that we understand the symbolic language of her unconscious, then that seemingly alien element of her reaction (the story of the plot, and the voices) becomes as 'understandable' to us and as logically motivated as the depression itself.

In other words, the amateur or untrained psychologist

(anybody with common sense) understands this woman's abnormal exaggerated grief reaction, but a psycho-analytically trained person is theoretically capable of understanding the superimposed elements of insanity. I say 'theoretically' because in order to understand them he would have to know not only the immediately preceding experience, the sudden bereavement, but many remote facts of our patient's history. However, in principle the causal connection which enters into this process of 'understanding' is the same—it is a psychic connection, a connection of cause and effect in the psychic order.

According to psycho-analysis, our patient's condition *appears* to consist of two elements: one which is familiar to everybody, namely, the seriously aggravated state of mourning; and one which is 'alien,' namely, the plot, the voices, and so on. In reality, there is no such division. It is only that the first one is immediately understandable, and the second remotely understandable. The first element every human being understands who ever mourned a loss. The second one is understandable only to those who have acquired a particular kind of insight. But it *is* understandable, and that is the most important thing of all.

I have stated that for this second mechanism of understanding, the one employed by psycho-analysis, we need to know something about 'the symbolic language of the unconscious.' Perhaps another example will help to explain exactly what this means.

John L., a man in his sixties, was brought to the hospital following an attempt at suicide. He had been depressed and anxious for three weeks preceding his abortive attempt to throw himself from a high building.

John had been born in a Scandinavian country in 1877,

one of a family of nine children. The father had married twice and John was the youngest of five children of the first marriage. The remaining four children of this marriage were girls. He was one and a half years old when his mother died, and six years old when his father remarried. The stepmother was not readily accepted into the family by the children, and the oldest daughter, aged seventeen, left home at that time. The patient, of course, had no recollection of his mother.

John's father and stepmother were very strict with him. He was always afraid of them, although he recalled that, when he was fifteen, he and his stepmother were good friends. On the other hand, he stated that his stepmother 'was always complaining to my father against me,' and this made John afraid of her. He felt that she favoured her own children to the disadvantage of himself and his full sisters, and the latter always felt resentful about this. He said that he was not a wilful or ill-tempered child, although he often tried to get his own way by fighting for it—but these attempts were never successful. At one point, while giving his history, he said, 'I never knew exactly where I belonged.' He said that he was a tidy child because he was compelled to be so, and he was now pleased with his early training because he had since found it useful in looking after himself.

He stated quite definitely that his childhood was unhappy because of the strictness of his parents, and that he was rather glad when, at the age of ten, he was sent away to boarding school. This change was a relief and he was sorry when the end of the school term came along and he had to go home on vacation. His father was a farmer, who worked hard for a living, but he usually had adequate means. At times, John helped on the farm.

He continued his studies at the boarding school for six years. He did well but he left for financial reasons before completing the final class. He had enjoyed school, where he had been a good mixer. He said he never felt particularly shy; he liked certain games, such as football, and he was fond of ski-ing.

After leaving school at sixteen, he became a clerical worker in the office of an importing firm. After working there for six years, he became a clerk in a department store. He enjoyed selling, and he liked his job. However, he left Scandinavia for the United States in 1909 at the age of thirty-two. When asked why he left his homeland, he spoke of the 'Viking instinct'—he wanted to see the world. He also said that he was disappointed in his hope of marriage at the time. I noted that his family name was Anglo-Saxon; but when questioned about this, he said it was also typically Scandinavian.

Later information, obtained from another source, revealed that his leaving his home country was more or less a flight: he had actually embezzled some money and apparently was about to be prosecuted. Soon afterwards, he changed his name from the Scandinavian to a similar-sounding Anglo-Saxon one.

John arrived in New York a friendless stranger but with the ability to speak English. He had already saved some money and had no apprehension about the future. He planned to go to California and started by way of New Orleans. However, in New Orleans he became acquainted with some business men and, through these contacts, succeeded in establishing himself in a small haberdashery. He ran this shop for five months and was doing rather well but found that he could not tolerate the heat. Because of this, he returned to New York and found work there. After three months, a job was offered to him in Ontario at one of the Canadian branches of a chain of men's clothing stores. He spent a year there. He was very successful in his management of this store and as a result was promoted in 1911 to the supervision of one of the larger branch stores in Montreal, where he remained ever since.

He was a hard worker by any standards. He would begin the day at 6 or 7 a.m. and frequently work until 10.30 at night, with very brief intervals for meals and only an occasional rest period, which he would spend lying down in his office at the back of the store. During the last few years before admission to the hospital, he had not been working at night because of fatigue at the end of the day. He usually bought food for his evening meal on the way home and felt that this, together with the actual preparation of the meal, was a tiresome chore.

He used to smoke approximately fifteen cigarettes daily but had recently been smoking about twice this amount. He enjoyed alcohol, at present mostly brandy, but was never a heavy drinker. His sleep had always been good, even the last few weeks before the attempted suicide, and only occasionally did he have a broken night. Of late, his memory for names seemed to be impaired but he had had no difficulty in managing his work or keeping the financial records at the store. He had not been making errors in accounts.

John gave up his social activities during the past few years because of his fatigue at night. He had once been a keen reader and enjoyed history and biography; he was fond of music and drama; but in recent years he had confined himself solely to reading the newspapers. Since settling in Montreal, he had had very little time for sports.

He was unmarried. As a young man, while living in

Scandinavia, he had been engaged twice. He broke the first engagement himself because, as he put it, his material prospects at the time were rather poor. On the second occasion, he was about to become engaged to a wealthy girl, but her father opposed this and insisted that they should not even correspond for a year before becoming engaged. The girl complied with her father's wish, and John left Scandinavia shortly afterwards.

At home, any mention of sex had been taboo. As a boy and young man he associated freely and easily with girls. After emigrating, he never met a girl whom he desired to marry. He had always been discriminating and, as he put it, 'snooty' with regard to making friends with persons of either sex. He denied any difficulty in sexual adjustment. He had had sexual relations at intervals throughout his life, apparently never with any woman with whom he was emotionally deeply involved.

He was not worried about money except for the present fear that he would not be allowed to carry on at his store and consequently lose his main source of income. He had had no financial losses.

This patient denied ever having had any previous attacks of depression or anxiety. However, it was learned that in 1937 he had been admitted to a Montreal hospital in a state of unconsciousness, and the diagnosis of barbiturate poisoning was made. His present sickness came on immediately after he had experienced certain difficulties with the authorities with regard to his business licence. While this enquiry was under way, the question of his citizenship came up. The authorities discovered that he had lost the citizenship of his home country, merely by allowing it to lapse; and, since he had never applied for Canadian citizenship, he was technically stateless. The situation produced in him a sudden despondency and gloomy outlook. He visualized his business taken away from him and thought he would be deported by the Canadian authorities. He saw himself arriving at a Scandinavian port as an old man, only to be rejected by his homeland because of the fact that he had lost his citizenship there. His home country would send him back to Canada without permission to enter, and he dejectedly pictured himself in his declining years, an unfortunate old man shuttled back and forth across the ocean without permission to enter either country.

The patient was neatly dressed, co-operative, though somewhat constrained. He walked and talked slowly and his facial expression was one of depression. He said that he felt depressed, admitted that he planned to commit suicide and said that it was not just an act of impulse. However, he admitted that he had hesitated just at the point of jumping from the window. The main content of his spontaneous remarks was his preoccupation with the question of citizenship. The idea that he would be shuttled back and forth across the ocean seemed to haunt him.

His orientation with regard to time, place, and person was intact. His memory for both recent and remote events was good. His mental capacity of retention and recall was not tested. He had a good grasp of facts of general information and his intelligence and judgment seemed to be good.

He had some insight into the nature of his condition in so far as he realized that he was suffering from a depression. He was unaware of the fact that there was something morbid about his preoccupation with certain ideas, such as that of wandering homeless between two countries. However, he felt that once the question of his citizenship was solved, his depression would clear up.

Contact was made with the consulate of his homeland

in Montreal to help John with his problem. It was through the consulate that it was learned that a short time before he left his homeland, in 1909, he had embezzled money. He evidently had to leave his country to avoid going to jail. It was also through this enquiry that we found out that John had changed his name to an Anglo-Saxon one similar to the Scandinavian original. The officials of his country were aware of his history and also knew that, except for his one transgression of the law, he had a clean record. It was evident that John had never applied for an extension of his citizenship or for naturalization because in doing so he would inevitably have disclosed the skeleton in his cupboard.

The physicians at the hospital never let the patient know that they were aware of his true history. However, when this critical period of his life, dating back thirty-five years, was discussed or when the question of his real name came up, a certain tension and restlessness were observed.

Finally, a meeting between the patient and the consul-general was arranged. The latter was an old gentleman in his eighties, considerably older than the patient himself, with a rather fatherly attitude and a remarkable understanding of our patient's peculiar situation and the psychological concomitants. After discussing the matter of citizenship with John, the consul laid all the cards on the table and told him frankly that his full history was well known to the officials, but that there was now no danger whatever of legal involvement and that everything had been 'forgiven and forgotten.'

This interview had a dramatic and striking effect on the patient; he recovered visibly within a short time and was able to be discharged one week later.

\*　　　\*　　　\*

Let us submit this story first to an amateur psychologist
—that is, to a person who knows nothing about the science
of psychiatry or psycho-analysis. There is a lot in this story
which he will immediately understand. The insecurity of
old age is a fact only too well known in our time. Here is
an old man who suddenly becomes aware of the possibility
of having his source of livelihood cut off. He has been
working hard for several decades, foreseeing an old age of
relative security. If you add to this the problem of citizenship, the papers and documents with their symbolic meaning of 'belonging,' the confirmation of 'self,' the story
becomes highly understandable. Almost anyone might
become depressed and anxious under such circumstances,
and quite a few would be driven to despair and suicide.

However, there is a part of John's story which seems to
exceed what we might expect of ourselves if we were in
the patient's shoes. It is the fantasy of the two countries
refusing entry so that one would be shuttled back and
forth across the ocean for the rest of one's life. To be
sure, the world of Immigration Departments, Passport
Control offices, and Police Stations represents a haunting
atmosphere for a great number of people, and there is a
lot of objective reality to justify such feeling. Nor is the
experience of being shuttled back and forth between two
countries beyond the realm of possibility, as the recently
publicized case of the man who lived on a ferry-boat in
the Far East confirms. Nevertheless, there was a bizarre
element about John's fantasy, particularly about the per-
sistence with which it was held, and the psycho-analytic
interpretation is as follows:

Country—in the language of our dreams, in the metaphors of everyday speech, and in the language of poets—
has a *parental* significance. It is not a coincidence that we

speak of 'fatherland' (*patria*), of 'Mother Earth,' and so on. To those who work with psycho-analytical concepts, it is not surprising and it is at the same time most important to know that John's history, from his early life, is typical of the 'rejected child.' It can easily be visualized how he must, in his childhood fantasies, have been running back and forth between father (fatherland) and stepmother (foreign land), being refused a port of entry, a harbour of acceptance and of sheltering.

Here we have made an important discovery. In dealing with John's situation, we are confronted with two worlds. There is the world of manifest reality, with its real and objective sources of anxiety—the insecurity of old age, of the expatriate, the guilt and anxiety about a skeleton in the cupboard. But the other world, behind this one, is the world of infantile fantasies which is no less fear-inspiring than the world of objective reality. Of this second world the patient is only partly conscious. However, these worlds are not independent of one another. There exists a living bond between the two, a relationship which is called *dynamic*. The fantasy of being shuttled back and forth across the ocean without permission to enter either of the two ports would not be so overpowering if it did not correspond to an infantile feeling of an entirely different content—namely, the feeling of being pushed away by father and stepmother. In fact, we have very strong reason to believe that our patient would have been able to handle the real and objective elements of insecurity in his life, had it not been for the fact that his present situation reactivated feelings which were buried but not dead.

We do not wish here to go into many other relevant things: the possible motivations for the embezzlement, the nature of the patient's guilt feelings, the way he apparently drove himself at work throughout his life in Canada, and the mechanism of his suicidal ideas. But one thing should be pointed out. The consul of his home country brought about a striking cure of the patient's depression not only through the fact that he reassured him about his status as a one-time culprit and ex-citizen but because he, the consul, represented not only the 'fatherland,' a personal principle, but the *figure of a forgiving and loving father*. The accidental age difference between patient and consul helped the situation. In other words, just as the objective threats of the patient's real situation were tremendously reinforced by unresolved threats of an early, infantile origin, so was the cure reinforced by the fact that the man who did the reassuring in objective reality represented an archaic figure of profound emotional meaning. And there is something else—the scene of 'everything is forgotten and forgiven' had so powerful an effect because our patient carried around with him not only the image of a punishing, haunting father (an image which he was able to reconstruct, at least partially, from the conscious recollection of his childhood) but also the image of an understanding, loving, and forgiving father. In order to grasp the outcome of our story it helps us a lot if we assume that in both instances, the inability to enter either of the two countries as well as the final scene of reconciliation, our patient had an experience, metaphorically speaking, of 'having been here before.'

The appearance of the aged consul on the scene provided something identical with what the ancient Greeks called *katharsis*, a certain point of climax and relief in the action of a tragedy. We say in idiomatic English about a person who is beset by conflicts that he is 'all tied up in knots.' *Katharsis* in the language of the Greek dramatists is a disentanglement of knots, and it is precisely in this sense that Freud reintroduced the word into the terminology of psychologists.

It is noteworthy that the success we had with the consul-general was not accidental. The psychiatrist who got him into the picture was fully aware of the Freudian implications of the case. He introduced the scene with the old consul quite consciously and intentionally as a cathartic, a 'deeply-stirring' element.

The reader who has no technical training in this field should stop for a moment and ask himself a simple question. When we continued beyond the point to which our amateur or naïve psychology had led us through empathy ('putting ourselves in his shoes'), we introduced tentative interpretations which do not immediately seem to have the character of evidence. If there is any evidence at all, is it the same as experimental evidence in the mathematical or biological sciences? Or are these interpretations (of the hidden motivations, the symbolic disguise) more closely related to empathy?

The answer is not difficult. The evidence of the world of archaic imagery behind the world of objective reality, and the dynamic relationship between the two, can be obtained by an empathic process rather than by the kind of methods used in the experimental sciences. (This does not mean that the method of proof as employed by the experimental sciences does not come in at all. As we shall see, it comes into the picture in a secondary way.)

We can summarize by saying that psycho-analysis has not only employed empathic knowledge as a scientific tool, it has done more: *it has pushed back the frontiers of empathy*. This fact is much more important than it may seem at first sight, and in the following chapters we shall see its historical significance.

Those who know anything about the history of science would assume off-hand that, in the history of psychology, knowledge gained by empathy *preceded* scientific knowledge and was replaced by it. 'Let's be more scientific' is, in the minds of most people, a motto for the progress of human thought, with 'scientific' in this connection meaning 'along the lines of the natural sciences.' From what we know about the history of Western thought, we would expect a scientific lecturer to say something like this:

'Before the advent of brain physiology, people used to explain cases like the one of the depressed patient, John L., with something resembling poetic intuition, comparing the fatherland to the father, the adopted country to the step-mother, and seeing in the patient's melancholy preoccupation an allegorical repetition of a childhood story. However, with the progress of science, it has been found that diseases of the mind are diseases of the brain. We know now that in our patient the function of the frontal lobe is disturbed in certain areas . . .'

The amazing fact is that the development of psychiatry was not at all like this. In fact, it was nearly the opposite! If we use science in the usual sense which implies laboratories, experiments, quantification and so on, we see that the development of psycho-analysis was *preceded* by the development of those methods or was simultaneous with it. Therefore, in order to understand what psycho-analysis is really about and how it is related to a certain philosophy of Man and the Universe, we have to study other trends of development in psychiatry. We have to look at psycho-analysis against the background of other sciences which developed during the past hundred years. This means a detour but later it will be seen that the detour is unavoidable if we want to come to grips with the real subject of this book.

# III    The Mechanics of Man

Oh, the nerves, the nerves; the mysteries of this machine
called Man!                                    DICKENS, *The Chimes*

THE history of psychiatry in the nineteenth century—
the background out of which psycho-analysis developed—is dominated chiefly by two trends. On one
hand, physicians strove to arrive at clear concepts of
diseases; on the other hand, they attempted to localize
mental functions in certain areas of the brain.

These two trends, although quite independent of each
other, are typical of the outlook which prevailed in general
medicine during that time. The first trend is summarized
by the word 'nosology.' Nosology (from the Greek *nosos*,
meaning illness) is the branch of medical science which
occupies itself with the classification and definition of
illnesses. In psychiatry this involved some tedious work,
and most of it was done in France and Germany, roughly
from the middle to the end of the century. At that time,
quite independently, the doctrine that 'mental diseases are
brain diseases' was established and the foundations laid
for the localization of mental functions in the brain. The
reader may well wonder: 'What's the practical use of
classifying diseases, and, even more so, what has it to do
with the present subject?' In order to explain, we have to

43

recount briefly the position of nosology in the history of medicine in general.

One hundred years ago there existed an illness called 'dropsy,' meaning an abnormal collection of fluid in the tissues of the body, particularly the abdomen and the legs. This disease has completely disappeared from the text-books. But it has not at all disappeared from our hospital wards. In adjoining hospital beds you may see two patients with an abnormal collection of fluid in abdomen and legs. Though they resemble each other closely, so much so that you are convinced that they suffer from the same condition, it turns out that one is the victim of a certain heart condi-tion and the other of a certain condition of the kidneys. The symptoms are similar, but the mechanisms behind the symptoms are quite different; needless to say, the treat-ment differs too. In a third bed you see a thin and emaciated patient whose body has collected very little fluid, yet you learn that he is suffering from the same kidney ailment, though in a different stage. In other words, as far as the three patients are concerned, you are baffled to discover that the two who resemble one another in symptoms differ in illness, and the two with different symptoms suffer from the same illness.

This shift of emphasis is extremely important, and it characterizes the entire development of medicine in the nineteenth century. The trend was to get away from *symptom concepts* (dropsy, consumption) to *diseases* (renal, cardiac diseases, tuberculosis, etc.); this development was inaugurated by morbid anatomy, bacteriology, and so on. It was, after all, the anatomist who discovered that the two seemingly identical cases of 'dropsy' were the outcome of two entirely different disturbances, as in our examples of the heart and of the kidney. There are trends in present-day medicine, in the mid-twentieth century, which modify all this; but the progress originally achieved by nosology cannot be estimated too highly.

One cannot blame the psychiatrists of the nineteenth century for wanting to follow in the footsteps of internal medicine. They felt that a similar development away from symptomatic concepts to 'true entities' was in order in their field. Originally the situation was quite similar to the one in medicine. What 'dropsy,' 'consumption,' and so on were to the physician, 'persecution mania,' 'religious mania,' 'stupor,' and so on were to the psychiatrist. Patients were labelled according to their prominent symptoms and their morbid preoccupations. Gradually psychiatrists began to realize that there was something beyond the symptom; that the psychiatric disorder followed some intrinsic law of development of which 'persecution mania' or 'stupor' were only external manifestations, just as 'dropsy' and 'consumption' may be two different manifestations of the same process in the pathology of organs.

However, from the beginning psychiatrists worked under a decisive handicap. We have seen that 'dropsy' had to be abandoned as a concept, after a sufficiently great number of cases had been studied at post-mortem; it was only by this method that it was possible to see in how many different ways 'dropsy' can come about. In psychiatry all attempts to come to a true concept of illness seemed to be doomed from the outset because in the majority of psychiatric disorders there are no abnormal findings at post-mortem. In the majority of cases, no matter how deranged they have been during life, at post-mortem the brain is normal even under the most powerful microscope. Therefore morbid anatomy, under whose influence the entire aspect of medicine was vastly changed during the

nineteenth century, was of help to the psychiatrist only in
that minority of illnesses in which one is able to find lesions
of the brain. In that minority, as we shall presently see,
considerable progress was achieved in a certain direction.
But the psychiatrists found that about four-fifths of the
population of 'asylums' was made up of patients whose
central nervous systems were, to all intents and purposes,
anatomically healthy. If psychiatry still insisted in imitating
the development of internal medicine ('from symptom
to disease'!), it had to try other avenues. And so the
psychiatrists of the French and German school began to
study the life histories of thousands of mental patients with
the most tedious and painstaking methods.

The results were quite startling. It would lead us too far
to go into details; it is enough to say that the outcome was
comparable to what we have seen in internal medicine.
You may find, in a psychiatric hospital, one patient who
looks as lifeless as a statue and another who is in a state
of extreme agitation and frenzy, and it may surprise you
to hear that these two conditions are external manifestations of the same thing. Today we know much better why
this should be so, but to a physician of the eighteenth
century it would have seemed meaningless or even paradoxical. Therefore one must not underestimate the historical
significance of the 'nosological' trend of the nineteenth century, although today its value has to a certain extent become
relative and questionable.

If we are able to say that the listless patient and the
agitated patient present opposite manifestations of disturbances which are, in a mysterious intrinsic manner,
*identical*, our nineteenth-century psychiatrist made this
important discovery by a method which is purely descriptive. If we take *cross-sections* of the lives of the two patients

at the time of their respective illnesses, we find, of course, that they suffer from two things which are contrary in all their qualities. It is only in studying hundreds of entire life histories in a *longitudinal* way, as it were, that one discovers that the two dissimilar states seem to replace each other so much that one comes to the conclusion that they must be haphazardly different expressions of the same thing.

As I have said, this method is purely descriptive. The patients' lives are treated as externalized objects. Empathy does not enter into it. That nineteenth-century school investigated mental sufferings as if they were psychic *objects* of which one can establish a psychic *morphology*. Though this is scientifically quite valid, its limits are narrow and its scope is soon exhausted. Moreover, it is intimately associated with mechanistic tendencies. If groups of disorders are established in the same manner in which one classifies species in general, one's outlook on psychiatry is bound to point in certain directions. That entire approach contributed, for example, to an attitude of biological determinism. If there are patterns of mental sickness which can be labelled and pigeon-holed in groups, the most obvious conclusion is that human lives are 'processes,' that the drama of an Ophelia or a King Lear rolls inexorably off a tape which has its origin in a constellation of chromosomes and chemical molecules.

The nosological movement in psychiatry, historically important as it was, is intimately linked with biological determinism, perhaps not so much as a well-defined philosophy but as a philosophical 'atmosphere.' Therefore the reader will not be surprised to find that there exists a historical connection between this movement on one hand and the eugenic outlook of the Nazis on the other. The establishment of 'true disease entities' was finally linked to a policy of sterilization which aimed at extirpating mental agony by crude methods of biological selection. Of course, the nosological psychiatrists cannot be blamed for this. It is mentioned only to illustrate to what extent their work of description and classification implied the existence, in mankind, of predetermined types. Biological determinism means not only this, however. It also implies that, as long as suffering can be studied as a classifiable and repetitive pattern, it must be left alone until the power of our microscopes and our chemical methods is enough advanced so that we can do something about it.

From a psychological point of view, from the point of view of what happens in the encounter of physician and patient as two human beings, the descriptive approach made for a marked therapeutic pessimism. It could not be otherwise. Disease was studied as if it were an externalized object; the highest aim was to ape the disease concept of internal medicine. Therefore there was only one place from which help could be expected—the laboratory.

Before we go on to give the reader a glimpse into the world of the laboratory we should, in passing, mention another movement which is related to the science of classification—the movement of phenomenology. This movement has been strong on the Continent, particularly in Germany and France. It originated with modern German philosophers, particularly Edmund Husserl and Karl Jaspers.

Phenomenology is essentially a descriptive science. Its essence is to study psychic phenomena as they are. What does the world in which a melancholy man moves really look like? What is the difference between our everyday suspicions and an insane person's ideas of persecution? Phenomenology gives as accurately as possible an inside view of our mental states but does not attempt to interpret them in the way in which we interpreted our case history. Moreover, it does not aim at treatment. Therefore it, too, often ends up with an attitude of describing, comparing, and labelling.

Phenomenology is mentioned here not only because the term will occasionally be used in these pages later, but also because the phenomenological trend in psychiatry is closely related to those interesting border areas between psychology and philosophy which we encounter in the existentialist writers.

Psychiatry in the nineteenth century was also dominated by the axiom, 'Diseases of the mind are diseases of the brain.' The implication was that, with a knowledge of the mechanism of the function of various brain centres, we were bound to explain all deviation of experience and of behaviour. Descartes had said that the human organism can be compared to a clockwork. Büchner taught that the brain secretes thoughts as the liver secretes bile.

The first steps in this direction did not appear propitious. Around the second decade of the nineteenth century there lived first in Vienna and later in Paris a fashionable doctor, named Gall, who claimed to be able to localize nearly all traits of a human person in various areas of the brain. He did this by palpating the surface of the skull. It is hard today to understand his tremendous success but there it was, one of the great social fads in medical history. (Even in Balzac's novels sophisticated characters in Paris drawing-rooms described a person as not possessing the bump of paternal love.) Gall's methods of scientific discovery were peculiar, to put it mildly. For example, it struck him that people with a great ability to express themselves through the spoken word had rather protruding eyes. From this he concluded that in these people the frontal part of the brain must be very well developed so as to push the eyes forward and hence he felt that the faculty of speech in man must be localized in the frontal lobe of the brain.

The amazing thing was that in 1848, thirty years after the publication of Gall's work, Bouillaud, an ardent admirer of Gall, did find a connection between lesions of the frontal lobes of the brain and an impairment of the function of speech! In 1861 a French physician, Broca, was able to relate the loss of articulated speech to circum-scribed lesions of a certain part of the left frontal lobe. Broca found that, in spite of the brain lesion, his patient's speech muscles were not at all paralysed. The patient was able to move the muscles of the lips, the cheeks, the tongue, the palate, the larynx—yet that meaningful harmonious synthesis of muscular movement which makes a spoken word was somehow lost. For example, in order to say the word 'bright' we have not only to be able to make the B sound (with our lips), the R sound (with our tongue), the I sound (with a combination of movements of respiratory muscles, larynx, and throat), and the T sound (with tongue and teeth). The totality of the sound 'bright' is not just a mathematical summation of all those noises. Something new has been produced, and although all the simple relay stations in the brain for these simple components (their location is known) may be intact, the motor-pattern 'bright' somehow does not come about when a certain area in the brain surface is destroyed. In 1865, two doctors by the name of Dax, father and son, showed that in the majority of people such lesions would have to occur on the left side of the brain.

The British neurologist, Bastian, in 1869 was probably the first to claim that we think in words, and that word

and thought cannot be separated. Actually, since Bastian's
time a concept has crept into neuro-psychiatry, which keeps
coming up again and again in all the investigations on
'brain and mind'—an idea that motor patterns of words are
stored in a mysterious fashion inside brain convolutions,
ready to be reactivated when they are needed. Since then it
has been more or less implied that in the left third frontal
convolution the motor patterns of words were deposited
in some form of physical trace comparable to the relief of
a phonographic groove. The centres from which actual
simple motor commands go to the speech muscles (tongue,
pharynx, larynx, etc.) provide a sort of pick-up system.

In 1874 Wernicke discovered that lesions of the first
temporal convolution and adjoining areas (in most people
on the left side) produce a state in which the patient,
though hearing perfectly well, does not understand the
spoken word. This state in its pure form is a perfect counterpart to the state described by Broca. Just as in Broca's form
of 'aphasia' (cerebral speech disorder) the patient is able
to move the muscles necessary for the production of sounds
such as B, R, I, T, but has completely lost the motor plan
of that meaningful sound pattern 'bright,' a patient with
Wernicke's aphasia is able to perceive all the sounds which
make up the word 'bright' but these sounds do not arrange
themselves into a meaningful acoustic pattern. He hears
a sentence but to him it remains a hodge-podge of sounds,
an experience similar to the one we all have when listening
to a foreign language. It is noteworthy that such patients
are able to talk freely (unlike a 'Broca' case); in fact, they
often talk too much, probably out of their feeling of
inadequacy. But their speech is a meaningless conglomerate
of words because they are unable to do what we do automatically all the time—control the meaning, grammar, and

syntax of our words by understanding what we ourselves are saying.

Soon after Wernicke's discovery, many other centres were located: one for reading, one for writing, one for calculating, one for music, and so on. The left hemisphere of the brain[1] was mapped out as a mosaic of centres of 'higher functions.' These centres are connected with association fibres. Disturbances such as aphasia, alexia (loss of the ability to read), agraphia (loss of the ability to write) were interpreted as destructions of centres or cutting off of their connections.

There is no doubt that some of the clinical observations of that time were a little forced to fit into this electrician's model of the human mind. This was later shown in critical studies by the great English neurologist, Sir Henry Head. However, the working concept achieved extraordinary triumphs. In at least one instance it was possible to predict the existence of a certain brain disorder on the basis of the anatomical diagram, and the postulated brain disorder was subsequently observed with the lesion exactly as predicted.[2]

[1] In left-handed people it is the *right* hemisphere.

[2] In lesions of the inferior part of the left parietal lobe a disturbance called apraxia is observed. The patient afflicted with this disorder is able to move both hands perfectly well and to recognize objects; yet he is not able to handle them properly. Confronted with a toothbrush, he might try to stuff it into his pocket; confronted with a pen, he might put it into his mouth. There is always a helpless and unco-ordinated fumbling. The interpretation was that there are stored in the left lower parietal lobe traces (our phonograph grooves) for complex patterns of motor activity in man. From this centre, fibres reach the motor centre (the 'pick-up' which actually gets the muscles of our hands into action) on the same side (left) and on the opposite side (right). The latter would have to pass through a complex bridge-like structure, the so-called *corpus callosum*. Hence Liepmann postulated in 1905 that in isolated circumscribed damage to the *corpus callosum*, those complex motor patterns of useful movements could not be projected from the left parietal area over to the motor centre on the right, and therefore in such a case the patient would suffer from an isolated apraxia in his left hand (the 'pick-up' motor centre on the right side of the brain controls the left hand). This clinico-anatomical picture, postulated by Liepmann in theoretical considerations, was actually observed in 1907 by Van Vlieten.

This was truly a triumph of the scientific method, comparable to those instances in the history of astronomy in which a star whose existence has been mathematically postulated is subsequently discovered. Nobody can blame the nineteenth-century scientist for becoming very enthusiastic over all this. The day did not seem far when every disturbance of thought, feeling, and willing would be a matter of 'centres' and 'pathways'—a few batteries exhausted here, a little wiring disconnected there. Descartes, with his clockwork, and Büchner with his thought-exuding organ had obviously entered the right path which would lead to the unravelling of that mystery—the human mind.

Of course, one might still argue that the disturbances observed in those cases of circumscribed brain lesions are fairly 'peripheral' when we consider the entirety of a human person. A person may lose his capacity to speak or to write or to recognize objects and so on, and yet certain basic features which we commonly associate with such terms as 'personality' or 'character' are not affected. Some readers may have encountered victims of cerebral stroke who suffered from speech disorders and who, in spite of being deprived of mechanisms of communication or even concept formation, did not seem altered in their basic features. Their goodness or warmth or humour, or their coldness, rigidity, or pedantry are still perceptible through a veil, as it were, of organic damage. Even marked impairment of memory may affect such traits of character surprisingly little.

On the other hand, rather early in the development which we are following here, observations seemed to indicate that the moral core of a person may be affected by the cutting of certain brain fibres. In 1868, during the building of the transcontinental railway in America, there occurred the famous case of the crowbar. During a blasting operation, a worker was hit in the forehead by a crowbar which sliced both frontal lobes from the rest of the brain. It is possible that the crowbar was affected by the heat of the blast and therefore sterilized because, in spite of this extensive brain operation under anything but aseptic conditions, no signs of local infection were observed and the workman lived. The result was a neat, quasi-experimental ablation of certain parts of the brain in a human subject. The psychological effect was remarkable. The workman who, up to the time of the accident, had apparently been puritanical to the point of rigidity, adopted the opposite 'pattern of behaviour.' He became dissipated and promiscuous; his actions were now facetious and cynical, and he swore like a trooper. Changes similar to the ones in this historical crowbar case were later encountered by many other observers in cases of lesions of the frontal lobes. To use the detached language of behaviouristic psychology, there was a 'loss of acquired inhibitions.' It is obvious that in such a case the personality, the character of the person, is much more altered than in the case of cerebral lesions which result in pure disturbances of cognitive function or communication.

Around the time of the First World War and in the years following, the text-book concepts of cerebral 'centres' and 'connections' for higher intellectual functions seemed to lose ground. The more one studied cases with detailed psychological methods and tried to correlate these findings with anatomical investigations, the more it became obvious that such functions as speech, recognition of objects, performance of delicate movements, and so on could not be explained on the basis of a mechanic's blueprint. Sir Henry Head, in presenting his own observations and at the same time subjecting the nineteenth-century school of brain localization to a critical analysis, began to make fun of the 'diagram makers' and their concept of the human psyche which came somewhat close to a plumber's ideal. This was the time of Bergson, of the phenomenological school of philosophy in Germany, and of the so-called Gestalt school of psychology.

The Gestalt school represented a movement to get away from the atomistic and mechanical concept in psychology which often leads to a superficial aping of the mathematical sciences but not to that which one wants to study. Employing methods of the so-called Gestalt school, Goldstein and Gelb studied a German soldier, Herr Schneider, who had received during the war a circumscribed lesion in the occipital lobe of the brain, in an area which has something to do with visual recognition. Their observations were published in an extensive work, entirely devoted to the strange world in which Schneider lived. The two scholars (one an eminent neurologist, the other an eminent psychologist) had practically lived with Herr Schneider for several years and succeeded to an uncanny degree in sharing this strange world of visual agnosia with him. What it actually amounted to was an extraordinary feat of empathy. Sir Henry Head hailed this work as marking the end of an era (that of the 'diagram-makers'), and the beginning of a new one. Philosophically speaking, the Cartesian utopia of a reconstruction of the 'human mind' on the basis of a model of centres with connecting wirings seemed to have vanished.

Long before that time, Hughlings Jackson, the father of modern neurology, had adopted a critical attitude towards 'centres' and 'diagrams.' The conception of chains of nerve cells and its application to clinical localization had led to such triumphs in neurology that it was only too tempting to apply the same concepts to higher intellectual functions. There is no greater sign of Hughlings Jackson's genius than the fact that, unlike his contemporaries, he resisted this temptation. With regard to such phenomena as speech disorders, he warned his students to 'consider our subject empirically and afterwards scientifically' and that 'to locate the damage which destroys speech, and to localize speech, are two different things.' This is a more simple expression of what Head meant when after an almost lifelong study of the subject he said that 'there are no cortical centres for normal mental activities, but there are certain areas within which destruction of tissue produces a disorder of some particular mode of behaviour.'

This is a very brief history of cerebral localization up to the 'twenties of this century. While the concept of the Cartesian clockwork was badly shaken by neurologists such as Head, Goldstein, Monakov, and Pierre Marie, by psychologists like those of the Gestalt school and by philosophers such as Bergson, it was at the same time buttressed from elsewhere. Here I should like to mention only two directions from which help came. One is the theory of the conditioned reflexes of Pavlov, the other is Watson's behaviourism.

Pavlov's reflexology can be briefly explained as follows. A reflex is an automatic reaction of the organism to a stimulus. This reaction is independent of consciousness. When one pricks a sleeping person's toe, he withdraws his foot. He does not necessarily wake up. What happens is this: the stimulus (pin-prick) sets off a biological reaction in a receptor organ of a nerve cell. This nerve cell belongs to the lower part of the spinal cord and sends a fine filament all the way down into the big toe. The reaction produced by the pin-prick travels at a speed of about two hundred miles per hour up to the spinal cord. There it is relayed to an entire battery of nerve cells with outgoing filaments which lead to muscles of the leg. A message is conveyed to these muscles to contract. This contraction is carried out so as to remove the toe from the danger zone.

When a dog is shown a piece of meat, his salivary glands and the mucous membrane of his stomach secrete a juice of a chemical composition which is needed for the digestion of meat. This, too, is a reflex. Professor Pavlov extended this simple experiment by sounding a certain tone whenever the piece of meat was held before the dog. After repeating this combination of stimuli (meat and tone), it was possible to obtain a secretion of digestive juice by sounding the tone alone, without producing the piece of meat. In other words an event—the tone, which is in no way associated with digestion—may be artificially isolated from the animal's total situation and be made to become a stimulus to digestion. This fact had been known empirically by animal trainers and circus people for many centuries. But it was scientifically evaluated first by Pavlov, and in an ingenious way elaborated to a theory which was to embrace the entire world of human conduct. Without further elaboration on our part, the reader can easily see why a theory of psychology which, in its roots, goes back to the principles of animal training should have become the officially proclaimed basis of psychology in the Soviet Union.

Behaviourism, chiefly associated with the name of Watson, is another approach to psychology which attempts to remain strictly scientific in a sense in which the school of brain physiology or the reflexology of Professor Pavlov are scientific. To make the theory of behaviourism best understood, let us refer once more to our initial remarks on the empathic function. A behaviourist would criticize our concept of empathy in words which might run approximately like this: 'The process of "understanding" which goes on while you are listening to a sad person's life story is not a scientific method. The variables are too great. How much you "understand" depends entirely on your own make-up, on your own background, your own life history, and on the mode in which your depressed patient expressed himself. The entire thing is purely subjective, and true science is objective.' Behaviourism attempts, in its method, to eliminate intuition and empathy as much as possible from the field of psychology. It relies to a large extent on the observation of animals, and works with the premise of a purely experimental setting, as if intuition did not exist. For example, as we shall see, a behaviourist might study the psychology of rivalry and competitiveness by studying the behaviour of a group of animals during feeding time and comparing it with the behaviour of children, attempting to use as much as possible methods with which we are familiar from the natural sciences, such as statistical analysis and graphs.

During and after the Second World War the neuro-physiological approach to the 'human mind' received a new impetus, comparable only with the one initiated by the first discovery of brain centres one hundred years before. It would not further our argument to go into the fascinating story of the electro-potentials registered from the normal and abnormal human brain, and the electrical stimulation of brain areas in conscious patients during brain operations. The reader who would like to study these phenomena is referred to technical manuals dealing with them. However, another subject should be mentioned here briefly—the science called 'cybernetics.'

With the development of the radio tube it was possible to develop calculating apparatuses to an incredible degree of perfection. As is well known, these machines are able to solve mathematical problems which a company of skilled mathematicians could not solve in a lifetime. They can also solve involved economic problems, problems of logistics for military purposes, and so on, as long as each problem can be fed into them in a certain form. A similar principle is employed in apparatuses which govern the activities of machines with complicated functions—for example, guided missiles. These apparatuses are able to receive information and to relay it to an executive mechanism in such a way that a desired course of action is maintained. If you are rowing a boat parallel to the shore of a lake and the current of the waves is such that your boat would be directed towards the middle of the lake, you correct this error more or less automatically, by the way in which you handle your oars. Now an automatic steering device registers the position of its rudder; if external forces have changed the rudder so as to endanger the desired course, the course is corrected. The device by which a machine exploits information received from outside to maintain its own steady course is called the 'feed-back.' This feed-back system has been evolved to such a height of perfection that mechanical steering devices are able to react with much greater reliability and accuracy than human beings do. The feed-back principle combined with the 'memory tube' (a tube which stores information) is able to achieve a lot of that which until recently has been strictly reserved to the function of the brain. Although one of the most recent calculators contains 23,000 valves and the human nervous system contains about fifteen billion cells, the basic principle is the same. Theoretically one ought to be able to construct a machine which functions like the human nervous system. The entire physiology of the human nervous system is based on exploiting information ('in-put'), in such a way as to maintain an even course.

When the scientists concerned with cybernetics venture predictions about the implications of their science in a future society, the reader who is a humanist gets goose-flesh. It is not so much the vision of machines with nervous system-like systems. It is when the science of cybernetics is applied to questions affecting the relations of human beings ('communicating animals') and the life of their society that we have to brace ourselves and take stock. However, before we do this, let us admit that Sir Henry Head rejoiced too early. What he thought had been the end of diagram-making was just the end of a prelude. The concepts of the people who had explained 'diseases of the mind as diseases of the brain' by drawing diagrams of centres with associations were simple in comparison with the development which has come about with present-day neurophysiology in conjunction with cybernetics. Indeed, it looks as if the era of the diagram-makers had just barely begun.

During what one might call the first phase in the history of brain physiology—the phase of Wernicke—the physiological diagrams were crude. At that time some critical psychiatrists advocated human understanding as opposed to scientific explaining, a re-experience of the patient's conflicts as opposed to a discovery of electric short-circuits. They scoffed at the physiological ideal and found a name for it—'brain mythology.' They may have been struck by the crudeness of the diagrams.

Now we have entered a second phase. The body of scientific facts has been very much expanded. The physical and mathematical foundations are much more solid. The new impulse which that movement has received by the methods of cybernetics is best characterized by quotations from Norbert Wiener's book:

Man, with the best developed nervous system of all the animals, with behaviour that probably depends on the longest chains of effectively operated neuronic chains, is then likely to perform a complicated type of behaviour efficiently very close to the edge of an overload, when he will give way in a serious and catastrophic way. This overload may take place in several ways: either by an excess in the amount of traffic to be carried, or by the excessive occupation of such channels by undesirable systems of traffic, like circulating memories which have increased to the extent of becoming pathological worries. In all these cases, a point will come—quite suddenly —when the normal traffic will not have space enough allotted to it, and we shall have a form of mental breakdown, very possibly amounting to insanity.

Thus the human brain would seem to be fairly efficient in the matter of the short-distance connectors, but quite defective in the matter of long-distance trunk lines. This means that in the case of a traffic jam, the processes involving parts of the brain quite remote from one another should suffer first. That is, processes involving several centres, a number of different motor processes, and a considerable number of association areas, should be among the least stable in cases of insanity. These are precisely the processes which we should normally class as higher, and we obtain another confirmation of our expectation, which seems to be verified by experience, that the higher processes deteriorate first in insanity.[1]

[1] Norbert Wiener, *Cybernetics*. John Wiley & Sons, Inc., 1951.

In this chapter we have grouped together several trends in the history of the mental sciences: the localization of brain function; Pavlov's physiology of conditioned reflexes; behaviourism; electro-physiology; cybernetics. All these seemingly ill-assorted disciplines have one thing in common. They study human actions with the same methods which are applied to the mechanics of inanimate matter. They are branches of the natural sciences. At least one of them, behaviourism, explicitly makes it part of its programme to get away from empathy, because of what it considers its lack of scientific validity.

Ingenious as these discoveries are—those in neurophysiology and localization represent triumphs in the history of science—the moment one's philosophy allows them to replace that which is gained by empathy—that is, by 'poetic,' non-scientific knowledge—one runs into a zone of absolute zero, a wasteland of dehumanization. In fact when the Russians hoped for a long time that brain physiology and a more and more intricate system of Pavlovian apparatuses would eventually solve all psychological problems, they were aiming towards an image of Man which is the only one compatible with the Marxist philosophy.

A 'science of human behaviour' which is exclusively based on physical data is a peculiar shadow-image of truth. Imagine the following Wellsian fantasy: At a time when all riddles of brain localization and neuro-physiology are solved, there exists a scientist who can really trace at once all the chemical processes in every cell of a brain and understand their interaction. That which is experienced as Hope and Despair, as Love and Hatred can be understood entirely in terms of neuronal and electronic mechanisms. Whatever melancholia means in terms of existence matters no longer. Knowing the area in which the brain cells are firing in the wrong direction, our scientist can regulate the disturbance hormonally or electrically. He is able to demonstrate with mathematical symbols what is going on in Hamlet's brain while he beholds his uncle in prayer. In fact he is even able to trace all the chemical processes and their casual sequence up to this point, right from Hamlet's birth. Though our scientist would be able to grasp the most extra-ordinary machine, what he grasps develops into a night-mare: the mystery of consciousness and, with it, human freedom and human values lie somewhere outside that machine.

Some of the scientists to whom we owe most in the field of brain localization have clearly seen this. But their insight is nothing new. Plato, as if he had foreseen behaviourism and neuro-physiology, outlined the philosophical pitfall with surprising clarity. He has Socrates in the *Phaedo* compare a man whose ideas on the human mind follow along these lines

to a person who began by maintaining generally that mind is the cause of the actions of Socrates, but who, when he endeavoured to explain the causes of my several actions in detail, went on to show that I sit here because my body is made up of bones and muscles; and the bones, as he would say, are hard and have joints which divide them, and the muscles are elastic, and they cover the bones, which have also a covering or environment of flesh and skin which contains them; and as the bones are lifted at their joints by the contraction or relaxation of the muscles, I am able to bend my limbs, and this is why I am sitting here in a curved posture—that is what he would say; and he would have a similar explanation of my talking to you, which he would attribute to sound, and air, and hearing, and he would assign ten thousand other causes of the same sort, forgetting to mention the true cause, which is, that the Athenians have thought fit to condemn me, and accordingly I have thought it better and more right to remain here and undergo my sentence; for I am inclined to think that these muscles and bones of mine would have gone off long ago to Megara or Boeotia—by the dog, they would, if they had been moved only by their own idea of what was best, and if I had not chosen the better and nobler part, instead of playing truant and running away, of enduring any punishment which the state inflicts. There is surely a strange confusion of causes and conditions in all this. It may be said, indeed, that without bones and muscles and the other parts of the body I cannot execute my purposes. But to say that I do as I do because of them, and that this is the way in which mind acts, and not from the choice of the best, is a very careless and idle mode of speaking. I wonder that they cannot distinguish the cause from the condition, which the many, feeling about in the dark, are always mistaking and misnaming.[1]

The opposite attitude has been expressed quite recently by Professor Bykov of the Soviet Academy of Science. After reviewing the most recent findings on the functioning of the brain, he expresses the hopes that 'we shall, in concert with capable and talented investigators throughout the world, be able to perceive the laws of thought, behaviour and instruction. This will mean that we are gaining the highest blessing—that of knowing ourselves.'[2] Though Bykov in this last phrase echoes Socrates' famous admonition ('know thyself'), he advocates what Socrates branded as a wrong method. The recent advances of brain physiology are wonderful, but the one thing they will obviously never

[1] *Phaedo*, translation by B. Jowett.
[2] K. M. Bykov, 'New Data on the Physiology and Pathology of the Cerebral Cortex,' U.S.S.R. State Academy of Science, Moscow, 1953.

bring about is knowledge of ourselves. Thus we see that a science—the physiology of the human nervous system—which is, like all science, philosophically neutral, achieves two contrasting meanings, depending on two different views regarding the nature of Man.

C

# IV     The Mechanics of Society

And Satan stood up against Israel, and provoked David to number Israel.

And David said to Joab, and to the rulers of the people, Go, number Israel, from Beer-sheba even to Dan; and bring the number of them to me, that I may know it.

And Joab answered, The Lord make his people an hundred times so many more as they be; but, my lord the king, are they not all my lord's servants? why then doth my lord require this thing? why will he be a cause of trespass to Israel?

I CHRONICLES 21: 1–3

To the statistician, the mass observer, you are one unit in a crowd. To a physicist you are a mathematical formula, to the chemist a compound of substances, to the biologist a specimen. The behaviourist sees you as an animal modified by conditioned reflexes. . . . So significant you are, so universally relevant. But how and by what right? Beware of asking; that way lies theology.     RONALD KNOX, *Stimuli*

IT is a natural reaction, when we read the history of scientific discoveries, to feel enthusiasm. Such discoveries are an expression of man's creativeness. When we trace the history of physics from Archimedes to the quantum theory; or the physiology of the heart from the time of Harvey up to the most recent discoveries on the stimulus conduction; or chemistry from Lavoisier to present-day biochemistry; or Doctor Bouillaud's research on the brain to modern discoveries on electro-physiology of the brain, we experience something which is a mixture of awe and æsthetic pleasure. 'An undevout astronomer,' wrote Edward Young in *Night Thoughts*, 'is mad.'

We feel alarmed, however, when a particular discipline of science assumes a *monistic* tendency, becomes all-explanatory, and even hints at utopian developments. When the 'brain mythologist' of the nineteenth century foresees a time in which all aberrations of the mind can be explained on the basis of false wirings, so that poetic and intuitive feelings can be excluded or invalidated, we are embarrassed. When the Marxist elevates the wired model man-machine—the *homme machine*—to a position which entirely occupies metaphysical space, we recognize it as a devilish distortion.

What is true about the mechanics of the human individual is equally true about the mechanics of human groups. The social sciences, particularly the psychological branches of sociology, are collecting a big conglomerate of observations on the reactions and interactions of groups of people. However, there is a great difference between doing this and doing the things described in the preceding chapter. In the latter the laboratory methods and the individual problems tackled are clear and unequivocal: one can make valuable studies of Pavlovian physiology without believing in Marxist philosophy; one can do research on localization in the brain and remain a good Christian. However, when the inter-action not of nerve cells but of groups of human individuals is studied, it frequently occurs that the validity of the method and the validity of the underlying philosophy of the social scientist become inextricably interlaced. This is a symptom of tremendous importance, and it marks an entirely new phase in the history of science.

Let us take a few random examples from the social sciences. First, there is something which might be called the magic of numbers—a widespread, though rather innocuous, obsession. Since quantification, the world of graphs and percentages, is associated with objectivity, some people feel its results must be 'truer' than statements which we conclude, by reasoning, to be right. That is why a quantitative analysis is often applied to a qualitative problem. Thus it is stated in a social psychological study on the 'pleasing personality'[1] that 'with women the multiple correlation between pleasingness and adjustment combined with expressiveness is ·71, and when steadiness is added to expressiveness the multiple correlation becomes ·79.' The author, equipped with mathematical tools ('difference divided by sigma of difference'), has tackled the following problem: 'When a person has personality, it is generally meant that he has a pleasing personality. Now what is a pleasing personality?' Evaluating the opinions given by individuals about members of their own and the opposite sex he observes, with scientific caution: 'Although the differences are not statistically reliable, it is interesting to note that men consider men less steady than women do; while women consider women less steady than they do men.' He immediately adds an interpretation of his findings (a procedure not quite scientific): 'This is undoubtedly a reflection of greater familiarity with one's own sex.' Using common sense, most people would arrive at a different interpretation, namely, rivalry with one's own sex.

Thus we see that we come up with nonsense if we give to the quantitative method a position of absolute primacy, and if we think that it is only by the quantitative method that we ascertain truth. What the scientist attempted to do in the present case was to settle a question of value with the aid of scientific method.

[1] Edwin G. Fleming, 'Pleasing Personality,' *Journal of Social Psychology*, III, 100-107, 1932.

One might argue that it is an error to introduce the scientific method into problems involving value, but that it is an error without serious consequence. This is not quite so. Whenever one introduces quantitative methods in an area in which a hierarchy of values exists, one is apt to corrode those values. In order to have numbers work properly they have to be on an equal basis. In order to add fifteen toadstools and fifteen roses, one has to make them into equal objects: fifteen toadstools and fifteen roses are thirty plants. To the person to whom the metaphysical has its intrinsic weight, quite independent of social references, a great deal of the social sciences is not as neutral as science should be. Because, in order to become numerical material, all that which is of the metaphysical order and which has meaning in the life of the individual soul has to be equalized with arbitrary elements of the social and economic order. Take, for example, the following table ('attitudes towards baptism') from a study which concerns the problem of conformity of opinions:

### TABLE[1]

| | Public attitude | | Private attitude | |
|---|---|---|---|---|
| | No. | % | No. | % |
| 1. In favour of sprinkling | 46 | 90.20 | 8 | 15.69 |
| 2. Either form of baptism | 4 | 7.84 | 36 | 70.59 |
| 3. In favour of immersion | — | — | 3 | 5.88 |
| 4. No attitude | 1 | 1.96 | 4 | 7.84 |

The author, who introduces certain statistical concepts into this problem ('the hypothesis of the J-shaped distribution

[1] From Richard L. Schanck, 'A Study of Change in Institutional Attitudes in a Rural Community,' *Journal of Social Psychology*, V, 121–128, 1934.

as a form of distribution characteristic of institutional behaviours'), states that 'it would seem probable that in the economic field objective checking on neighbours' behaviour would be easier than in the field of religion.' He believes '(1) that a feeling of community loyalty caused many of these individuals (the subjects under investigation) to believe the way they thought most people in the community believed, and (2) that biased individuals in the community who are given to the expression of their opinion tend to create an illusion regarding community opinion that not always corresponds with the real facts. Those who do the talking in the community tend to be taken as community spokesmen.' At this stage the naïve reader begins to be impressed. In fact this is the phase (so often observed in this kind of investigation) when something which we have known from common-sense observation is presented with mathematical under-pinnings. This air of objectivity is emphasized by the style: 'That these conclusions were not too far-fetched was strikingly illustrated at a later date . . .' or, 'It seems probable that there is a stage in attitude change when attitudes are maintained in a group because of illusions how universally the attitude is held by other members. This state is one which F. H. Allport has referred to as a condition of "pluralistic ignorance." ' Or, 'This making an entity of an institution (religious Church community) as the source or author of an opinion is one of the results of "pluralistic ignorance." ' The last sentence, if I understand the terminology correctly, means: People think that they ought to hold the same opinions as others. In certain matters (including religious ones) they are under an illusion about this. Their belief is not shared by others to the same degree as they think. Hence the difference between private and public attitude in the table. This mistake also causes them to believe that there is a Church which is a mother and keeper of faith.

It is quite possible that I misunderstand the meaning and aim of such studies, but one thing is certain. Whenever the bulldozer of statistics rolls through the flowering meadow, followed by the steamroller of socio-psychological evaluation, nothing can survive. One might argue that faith can be investigated on the natural, either social or psychological, plane and not emerge the worse for it. This is true but that is not our point. What we want to show here is that the very method itself, and the position of the problem, postulate an equalization. For science of this sort, supernatural values have to be dehydrated and hardened before they can be investigated. Take a sentence like this: 'Further investigations of this hypothesis are now being carried on in industrial, political, religious and economic fields.' The very way in which the word 'religious' is used in this sentence is alien to the Christian. Either the Church is the Mystical body of Christ, or it is nothing—a fascia in the social structure, arbitrarily accounted for somewhere between the 'political' and 'economic' fields.

It is doubtful whether Saint John the Baptist and Saint Paul foresaw this particular kind of paganism. But there is no doubt that they would have preferred to be beheaded or crucified by ancient pagans than see the sacrament of baptism and the community of saints benevolently reduced to percentile columns in a study on 'pluralistic ignorance.' Thus we can say that things such as 'religious attitudes' can be dealt with as elements of the social fabric, in statistical analyses, and in mass equations only on the basis of a fiction. They have first to be deprived of their metaphysical character, as it were, and treated as if they did not belong to the order of Grace.

The atmosphere of apparent objectivity in which the social psychologist works is actually a result and an expression of an urbane, technocratic civilization which squeezes the unique and mysterious element out of things which are of the spirit. A number of sociologists realize this paradox and have made attempts to deal with the 'problem of values.' Whenever we encounter values, however, we arrive at the point at which science stops.

Values—'good' and 'bad,' or 'beautiful' and 'ugly'—are not the object of science. A mathematician measuring a triangle or a circle, or relating the number 73 to the number 17, does not ask which one is beautiful, ugly, good, or bad. In the world of chemistry the carbon atom is in no way 'better' than the hydrogen atom. A zoologist, unless he is at the same time a poet, does not compare a rooster with a gander from a moral or æsthetic point of view—and if he does, he gets his poetry and his science badly mixed. In natural history, in the old days before the advent of modern science, people used to make statements about the lion being nobler than the wolf; of course, no scientist would say anything like this today. It is in the nature of scientific method that it has to exclude the world of values, the moral or æsthetic hierarchy of 'good' and 'bad,' in order to arrive at correct results.

Let us consider further what happens when we try to apply scientific method to the world of values—and we shall confine matters to æsthetic values, rather than spiritual or moral values. (It is interesting that a belief in æsthetic values is the one thing people hold on to longest. Even the most avowed amoralists and atheists believe in æsthetic values. Dostoievsky, who had such keen insight into the modern spiritual dilemma, once remarked that the world will be saved by Beauty. I have seen many atheists in rapture over a Bach fugue or Haydn quartet; they little realized that they would have to burn all the great musical scores in a bonfire if they really lived what they preached.) We say that certain things are more beautiful than others. A symphony of Mozart is more beautiful than jukebox music; a Rembrandt painting is more beautiful than a magazine cover. But there is no method in the social sciences which would help either to support or to deny this hierarchy of values. A sociologist might find, by questionnaire methods, that there are areas in which 93 per cent of all the people prefer magazine covers to Rembrandt paintings. In another area the reverse may be true. We might even find factors which would account for these differences in taste. Yet the question of intrinsic value —what makes one thing more beautiful than another— remains untouched.

A team of research workers might tackle Beethoven's Ninth Symphony over a period of ten years. The physicists on the team could make statistical studies and graphs of the acoustical wavelengths and amplitudes. The psychologists could scrutinize Beethoven's childhood history minutely. The social scientists could examine the European outlook at the end of the Napoleonic era. And so on. No matter how much data our scientific team compiled, it could not 'explain' a single bar of the musical experience we call the Ninth Symphony. Nor could the combined team come to any conclusion as to whether or not the Ninth Symphony is more beautiful than the latest hit from a musical show. From this example alone, we must conclude that there exists a great number of truths which are not accessible to what one commonly calls scientific investigation—i.e., to an area of human endeavour in which experiments, or numbers, or the accumulation of facts dominate. Values are transcendental. They lie in an area which accumulative knowledge cannot reach.

When Francis Bacon discussed the method of scientific investigation, he was far from claiming that it was the *only* method by which to find truth. On the contrary, he clearly distinguished scientific method from poetic insight. His genius saved him from the disastrous fallacy to which a great number of people succumb nowadays—*grading* these two different workings of the human mind, and believing that scientific truths are 'truer' than poetic truths. All Bacon said was that some insights are obtained in one way and others in another way. If he had pronounced a warning at all, he would probably have sounded one against applying 'Poesy' to truths which are only accessible to the scientific method. If he had been able to foresee our modern phase, he would no doubt have given the opposite warning. Some of the statements of the later schoolmen on scientific subjects are funny when read today just because of the simple confusion of methods of thinking.

The student of the social sciences who believes in spiritual values is particularly interested in those trends which are anti-human and which carry in themselves the seeds of negation. He soon encounters another fallacy which is closely related to the one just discussed. This fallacy may be stated as follows: Men have always known that apples fall to the ground, not up to the sky. However, only with the mathematical analysis of this phenomenon, as developed by classical physics, were laws formulated which eventually led to a knowledge and mastery of physical forces quite undreamed of before. In like manner, people have always 'known' about the 'forces' which govern the relationships between groups of human beings—such as rivalry and the formation of social hierarchies—yet our knowledge of these things is at present the same as our knowledge of inanimate nature before the time of Galileo. Only by the discovery of laws governing group relations comparable to the laws of classical physics can we arrive at a social science in the proper sense of the word.

This trend can be studied in its purest and most coherent form in cases where experimental psychology of animals is introduced with the explicit hope of discovering exact laws *which can then be applied to human beings*. Of course, in such experiments both empathy and moral value must be discarded as factors interfering with scientific validity.

An experimental psychologist, who had contributed important observations on the social psychology of animals, studied the mechanism of rivalry in *Gallus domesticus*, or the common rooster.

Beginning at sixteen weeks of age (he writes [1]) six young roosters are arranged in a hierarchy of dominance, the order being determined by the number of individuals in the group that each rooster is able to defeat in physical combat (Social Reflex No. 2). This order of ranking is revised at intervals of four weeks from the sixteenth to the thirty-sixth week. Beginning immediately after being taken from the incubator, these same individuals had been tested at frequent intervals in the Social Reflex Runway. This test consisted simply of releasing two individuals from opposite ends of the runway, and observing the time and distance traversed by each in running to the other (Social Reflex No. 1). Various operations from the techniques of physics were applied to these data. This was followed by the application of the simple measurements of time and space. When plotted as a function of Social Reflex No. 2, it was found that Social Reflex No. 1, when plotted in terms of space alone, was almost truly linear. A theoretical correction of the abscissa units, which agreed

[1] Carl Murchison, 'The experimental measurements of a social hierarchy in *Gallus domesticus*.' Also, 'The direct identification and direct measurement of Social Reflex No. 1 and Social Reflex No. 2,' *Journal of General Psychology*, XII, 3–39, 1935.

with the empirical data, satisfied the requirements of linear function. It was pointed out that this method of measurement and analysis was initiated as a result of reflecting on the discussion of the social sciences by Spektorsky, Sorokin, Har, and others to the effect that no genuine laws have ever been formulated in the field of social science. *It was pointed out that this or some similar method, built on the presupposition that the method operates on behaviour quanta common to the social conduct of all social animals, can reach through the medium of co-variable techniques to the eventual formulation of law.*

This last remark (the italics are mine) apparently includes human beings in the phrase, 'all social animals.' It is a fairly illustrative example. The mechanism of rivalry and competition is studied in an animal, the rooster, which is so familiar and well-known that it promises to be an excellent object for such a study. Definitions and experimental methods are as precise as they can possibly be. 'Social discrimination in *Gallus domesticus* is identified as it is measured in the Social Discrimination Cage.' As far as the social interaction and group behaviour of roosters goes, it is conceivable that we can 'arrive at the formulation of law' only by the discovery—'through the medium of co-variable techniques'—of 'behaviour quanta.' If 'social rivals' includes human beings, it is impossible to see how volumes of this science can tell us anything about man nearly as profound as Shakespeare tells us on one page.

However, as we have said, such a study of the rooster is valid for anyone who is interested in certain aspects of the behaviour of animals. A naïve 'optimism of the technique' comes in merely at the point where the investigator foresees a sort of physics of the interaction of living human beings in general. He vaguely postulates the possibility, and he is cautious in formulating it.

*       *       *

We are going many steps further when we consider certain trends in social psychology proper. The work of Jurgen Ruesch is fairly representative of this. In his studies, the physics of communication are applied to the study of interhuman relationships.

> Data pertaining to the ways and means by which people exchange messages, to the correction of information through social contact, and to action undertaken as an outgrowth of communication are handled successfully within the scientific model of communication. . . . The Communication Model is used with success whenever two or more biological or social entities have to be related to each other. Where the scientist has only one entity to contend with, the communication model is less suitable.[1]

Here the relationship of man to man is studied as if society consisted of entities comparable to the entities which the physicist studies. The investigator, deceiving himself into an attitude of concreteness and of handling primarily given data, handles his 'entities' so that in the end they become empty abstractions. He acknowledges the difference which exists between thinking human beings, animals, and pebbles. But he tries to force human relationship into a frame of physical references. Cybernetics, the 'feedback,' and Heisenberg's principle of indeterminacy contribute to the 'model.' The human encounter is projected on to a screen of physical matrices. It is noteworthy that for this to be possible the Hellenic concept of Man and human values has to be discarded; the Christian concept is not even mentioned.

In the traditional, class-theoretical, Aristotelian approach, an event was grouped with other events into classes

[1] Jurgen Ruesch, 'Synopsis of the Theory of Human Communication,' *Psychiatry*, XVI, 215–243, 1953.

dominated by similar characteristics. The establishment of a class of events was determined by the question of regularity in terms of frequency of recurrence, and therefore the individual case has no place in Aristotelian thinking. . . .

In the present-day, field-theoretical, Galilean approach, events are studied with respect to the field in which they take place, and an attempt is made to specify the conditions under which an event might occur. *Functions are conceived as forces; as a result value concepts, dichotomies, and other old-fashioned alternatives have gradually disappeared.*[1] Inasmuch as the laws in the field-theoretical approach are not based on class characteristics but upon the relationship between an object and its field, similar principles can be applied to a single case also. While in the traditional class-theoretical approach the characteristics of an object were completely determined in advance, in the field-theoretical approach the characteristics and dynamics of an object are determined by its relationship to the surroundings. In social science, the field-theoretical approach is more to the point than the class-theoretical approach because all human beings are surrounded by an environment and all scientific observations have to be made from some position located in the environment.[2]

This 'field-theoretical, Galilean approach' is actually Cartesianism pushed to an ultimate degree of absurdity. *Hommes machines* make up a *société machine*, and the living together of human beings is like the Bell Telephone System, though somewhat more complex. The premise—namely, to replace the 'class-theoretical, Aristotelian' approach by something concrete—is fictitious. The concreteness of the human subject is conjured away. Where there has once been the Community of Man there is now the Mechanism of Communication.

Something similar can be observed in a comparatively

[1] The italics are mine.
[2] *Ibid.*

recent psychological discipline, the study of group dynamics. This is a trend in research which occupies itself not with the single person but with groups of people or even with people *en masse*. There exist group dynamics 'laboratories' in which the relationships of persons are determined. With and without their knowledge, groups of human beings are observed in social intercourse through one-way mirrors, with phonographic gadgets. Rivalry and leadership, hostility and submission, the mechanisms of 'democracy' and of hierarchies are scientifically studied. 'Leaders' are being planted without the knowledge of the group—for the purpose of creating a definite psychological setting such as subordination or rejection. The point is that interactions of numbers of human beings are experimentally manipulated and in the end represented in graphs or other mathematical formulations—or somehow in the form of 'laws.' Here, too, the ideal (whether explicit or not does not make any difference) is that the social sciences should at some time reach a degree of exactitude and predictability which would match those of the natural sciences.

This is not only an academic fallacy. If this type of psychology, with the mechanisms of group formation, of hierarchical domination and so on, expressed in 'behaviour quanta' or in the 'communication model,' could lead to a revolution in group psychology comparable to the Newtonian revolution in physics, there would be only one result—the destruction of everything that human beings cherish.

As we shall later see, the perfect psychological situation between human beings is the real meeting of 'I' and 'Thou.' This situation differs in essence from the one which exists when man is confronted with inanimate nature—the meeting of 'I' and 'It.' In order to fit 'Thou' into a frame of mathematical references, you must be reduced to an 'It,' and thus the relationship becomes dehumanized. If anyone ever succeeded in establishing laws about the relationships of men to one another, comparable to the laws of physics, he would create a world in which metaphysical values have no place.[1] Freedom, love, and the personality itself would be denied. Everything that makes human relationships human would be lost.

It is obvious that not all social psychologists share the hopes of arriving at a physics of group mechanisms. Nor do they all work on the scientific premise of living in a valueless world. If, for instance, a scientist studies the mechanism of racial hatred in a social entity he must, consciously or not, assume moral laws which are anchored outside the area of his science.

Nevertheless, the world of our experimental psychologist, with his ideal of 'behaviour quanta,' merges imperceptibly into a large ill-defined area composed of social psychology, industrial psychology, and sociology, in which the relationships of human beings are studied in large groups, with the premise that human happiness and discontent can be studied scientifically in order to be engineered. The premise is a sort of scientific ideal. Human society is studied in a vacuum apparatus which has first been emptied of the breath of the gospel.

In the history of science, as Whitehead has shown, methods do not make their appearance in a haphazard way. They arise out of the general cultural atmosphere of the time. On the other hand new scientific methods, in

---

[1] This is the reason why many social psychologists who work on the 'model' refer to Bertrand Russell and John Dewey for their philosophical basis.

their turn, mould the cultural and social tissue. It stands to reason that the conglomerate of methods and the extreme methodological ideals associated with them should make their appearance at this moment, when industrialization and mass production make the smooth working-together and living-together of large numbers of people necessary.

As we have seen, these sciences must, at least to a large extent, work on the premise that there is no uniqueness and mystery to the person, or to his relationship with God, or to his relationship with other persons. Some of the more radical exponents of this trend postulate quite explicitly that anything of the metaphysical order has to be discarded if we want real progress in the direction of social engineering. K. R. Popper[1] observes quite correctly that 'the metaphysics of history impede the application of the piecemeal methods of science to the problems of social reform.'

'Piecemeal methods,' in this connection, is not a deprecatory expression. On the contrary, Popper, a physicist who ventured into this field because he had been 'interested for many years in the problem of the backwardness of the social sciences,' states that 'piecemeal social engineering' is our only salvation.

His argument runs as follows: All attempts at social engineering thus far in the course of history have been utopian, or at least have had some utopian element. Therefore they have all had somewhere in their origin an element of the metaphysical, the spiritual, the non-scientific, and thus tended to be authoritarian. Even the Marxist revolution, the biggest attempt at social engineering in modern history, in spite of its atheistic-rationalist philosophy, had

---

[1] K. R. Popper, *The Open Society and its Enemies*, Princeton University Press, 1950.

an undercurrent of faith and of religious ideal. It had a messianic and utopian taint, and was therefore doomed to fail in its aim. Or perhaps it had the wrong aim. At any rate, the author remarks that there is only one way to construct the machine of human society rationally and dispassionately, in the same manner in which the physicist works—you have to discard first anything which is, even in the remotest, of the spiritual order.

Popper advocates 'what I may term "piecemeal social engineering" in opposition to "utopian social engineering," ' not so much because the former works better (it is too early even for Popper to tell), but because the latter is invariably corrupted by a metaphysical idea. All the misery of Western man, his failure to run on scientific ball-bearings, is traced back to Plato who is treated throughout Mr Popper's book as Public Enemy Number One. Popper's survey has somehow the air of the Great Inquisition. He pursues with remarkable zeal his aim 'to further the transition from the tribal or "closed society" with its submission to magical forces, to the open society which sets free the critical powers of man.' From Aristotle, who is not quite as bad as Plato but bad enough, down through the course of history to Mr Toynbee, who gets poor marks in his capacity as a Christian but is recommended for his historical erudition, every suspect is investigated. In fact, the timid reader who does not agree with the author's ideas is bound to develop a vision of Popper's 'closed' society with himself left out in the 'open.'

This work is quoted here not because of its position in the current sociological literature. In fact, there are quite a few sociologists who seriously criticize it. It is quoted because it is symptomatic of a powerful trend in the present-day social sciences. In works of this sort we find the crystallization of a lot of elements which otherwise are still in flux.

In summary, let us repeat that there is, of course, 'nothing wrong' with the social sciences as such. Needless to say, the science of statistics, the observation of group relations, and all such things may in themselves be valuable. What Socrates said in the *Phaedo*, in comparison to Professor Bykov, also applies here: when our concept of values is distorted, when the idea of the human person and of human community is lost, then methods which are innocent in themselves become corrosive.

# V The Dawn of Psycho-analysis

> I not remembring how I cried out then
> Will cry it o'er again: it is a hint
> That wrings mine eyes to 't.
>
> SHAKESPEARE, *The Tempest*

> We are healed of a suffering only by experiencing it to the full.
> MARCEL PROUST, *The Sweet Cheat Gone*

WE return now to psycho-analysis. The argument of this book is historical in the widest sense of the word. An attempt is being made to follow the dialectics of ideas: to see how certain problems arose and how certain solutions came about. In this chapter we are going to outline psycho-analytical concepts as they originally developed.

Only if we look at psycho-analysis emerging, as it were, out of the background of the nineteenth century are we properly capable of understanding its historical meaning. Therefore in the present chapter we are laying emphasis more on the 'classical' than on the later periods of psycho-analysis. Psycho-analysis has developed into a huge body of observations, theoretical concepts, therapeutic methods. Freud himself corrected and changed some of his original concepts as time went on. Moreover, new schools began to split off from the Freudian tradition. Some of the more recent developments of Freudian psycho-analysis and of those derivative schools will be touched upon in the later chapters of this book whenever this is necessary from the point of view of our argument. Nor did psycho-analysis stop at the understanding and treatment of the neurotic patient, or the formation of a new psychology; quite early it began to deal with cultural and religious questions and with mankind *en masse*. This aspect will also be discussed in a later chapter.

In the middle 1890s Freud published, first with Breuer and later alone, a series of studies on hysteria. 'Hysteria' in the language of the psychiatrist is something different from 'hysteria' as used in everyday English. The latter word has the connotation of becoming 'emotional,' or excited and noisy. Hysteria in medical terminology is a condition which *imitates* a physical, frequently a neurological, disorder. For example, people with half-sided numbness of the body (hemi-anæsthesia) are usually victims of a lesion, such as a hæmorrhage, in certain parts of the nervous system which are concerned with the function of sensation. However, a condition of hemi-anæsthesia may also occur in a patient without any organic lesion of the nervous system whatsoever. Such a symptom (provided that the patient is not a malingerer—that is, intentionally and purposefully faking a sickness) is called hysterical.

Until 1894, hysterical symptoms were defined precisely in such a negative way—by the absence of any organic lesion which would account for their presence. With the observations of Freud and Breuer the hysterical symptoms received a more positive definition for the first time. Let us imagine that a soldier returns from an extremely harassing experience in combat (say at Dunkirk) with hysterical blindness. This means that he is blind, but without evidence of organic lesion of the visual apparatus from cornea to the visual cortex of the brain. This soldier is subjected to hypnotic sessions (with or without pharmaceutic aid) and given the hypnotic suggestion of battle experiences under Dunkirk-like conditions. He recalls, under hypnosis, many dreadful details which he cannot recall under the ordinary wakeful conditions of history-taking. At the same time he yells and cries like a child under the influence of something horrifying. As he wakes up from this session, he may have regained his eyesight.

In Freudian terminology, the original horrifying experience (Dunkirk) is called 'trauma' (wound). The inability to recall some of the most wounding details of the experience is called 'repression.' The lively recall under hypnosis is called 'abreaction' or 'acting out' or *catharsis.*' All these concepts are well known to most people today because everyone has done a certain amount of reading in abnormal psychology. Now let us consider the theoretical concepts which Freud introduced to explain his observations. Our soldier's first reaction (like anybody else's) might have been to cry and yell in horror when he was cut off from his unit, cornered with no chance of escape, and shot at from all sides. However, he did not give way to this impulse because it is 'cowardly'—that is, not compatible with accepted moral standards. Now there exists in the psychic universe of each person a law of conservation of emotional tension which is comparable to the law of conservation of physical energy in nature. The 'amount' of emotional tension repressed cannot just vanish. It is directed into another channel and it reappears under the formation of a symptom (blindness). The symptom is produced by a 'conversion' (transformation) of emotional tension. Under hypnosis the emotional tension finds an outlet which had first been blocked: the patient yells and cries with horror, and with this reconversion the symptom of blindness disappears. This is the reason why this type of hysteria has since the early studies of Freud and Breuer been generally called 'conversion' hysteria—the idea of the hysterical symptoms being something into which 'psychic energy' has been 'converted.'

These early investigations were the test-tube experiment, the small-scale model of all that psycho-analysis later developed into. Soon it was found out that the overt psychic injury (Dunkirk) was only a superficial immediate cause. It was one link in a chain, or rather in an involved net of chains which reached right back into the dawn of the patient's history.

In other words, the idea of *the* trauma had to be abandoned. There was rather a multiple set of traumas. It looked almost as if life itself had been a tissue of injuries and, what was even more astonishing, the earlier one went back into the patient's past the more traumatizing the events seem to have been. In order to understand this better, one may illustrate it with the biology of physical wounds, and with certain observations on the subjective experience of time. Microscopically small wounds inflicted on embryonic tissue in experimental embryology have a more fundamental effect on the structure of the mature organism the earlier they are inflicted. A small cut which would escape notice if inflicted on the mature body after birth can produce entire malformations if applied to the embryo. The malformation is more monstrous the earlier the cut occurs. If we assume that a similar law exists in our psychic development, we understand much better why things which go wrong in a minor way ('minor' by grown-up standards) may have a tremendous impact on the formation of habits and on the structure of character when they happen early in life to a psychic tissue which, like embryonic tissue, is still fully charged with potentialities.

Moreover, we know from careful biological and psychological studies that one's idea and experience of time changes in a way which represents the inverse ratio of a person's age. Everybody knows that, as we grow older, time seems to move faster. When we think back to our childhood, one springtime seemed to be separated from the next by ages. As life goes on, the seasons move closer together. For an old man the past ten years seem to have succeeded each other rapidly. In the same way, the first few years of infancy seem æons long, and the first few days an eternity.

Thus, contrary to our test-tube example—the story of the blind soldier—the trauma which stands out in such a striking way has to be replaced by a vast multiplicity of experiences. This is also true as far as the symptom is concerned. Sudden blindness—one outstanding illness—appears in the history of our patient like a sharply-defined, punched-out event. Such cases of conversion hysteria are not frequent nowadays, and readers who are not physicians will see very few of them in a lifetime.

In a patient who complains of the fact that he feels tense in the presence of strangers, that he has an experience of anxiety when he is newly introduced to someone, that he suffers from insomnia, from stomach ache, headache and from lower back pain, the situation is quite different. His complaints are diffuse, there are several of them, and more often than not he is unable to give a definite time at which all this began. Thus we see that in contrast to the first observations which initiated the psycho-analytic development, in most cases we are far from having to deal with one symptom, occurring suddenly. We would invariably be wrong if we assumed the existence of *one* trauma, the punched-out event. Quite early it was discovered that hypnosis is a poor method to investigate the unconscious significance of a symptom and to heal it; there are much better methods for this.

The basic principle of psycho-analysis was nevertheless contained in the very first writings of sixty years ago. Experiences are stowed away into something which is called the unconscious; the emotional tension associated with them cannot vanish into nothingness; the neurotic symptom is the product of a metamorphosis. Whatever has been withheld from conscious life, for any reason, breaks back into it under disguise.

Even at this early stage the concept of the unconscious had acquired something peculiar. The existence of an unconscious was nothing new. It was known that the material of things remembered is stored away in us somewhere outside consciousness. If someone asks you how much three times seven is, you do not calculate; you answer from memory. But since you have not been thinking of the solution before you were asked, you must have produced it from some unlit corner of your mind. This is the neutral, bland concept of the unconscious of the classical phase of experimental psychology. However, in cases of conversion hysteria the unconscious was not bland. It acted as if it withdrew certain elements because they were too heavy to bear, released them again in clever disguise, and could only with difficulty be tricked into releasing them with their full charge of feeling. The relationship between the conscious and the unconscious part of the mind was, quite contrary to the simple example of learned material, part of the human drama. The relationship was, as we put it nowadays, *dynamic*—a term we have already explained in the case history of the old immigrant. Our blind soldier, while spectator and part of a scene of horror, had been under a moral conflict. His eyes said: 'We do not want to see!' In order to trace symptoms back along the stream of the psychic, along thousands of rivulets into their hidden origins, methods much better than that of hypnosis had to be employed. One of these methods was the free association of thoughts.

Most of our thinking during the day, particularly when we talk, is directed towards a goal. We intentionally set out to think about something, or we want to get something across. Thus our trend of thinking is shaped into a pattern. It has a theme. It rarely happens that our thoughts float freely without any mapped-out direction. This occurs only in certain situations—for example, for a short while before we fall asleep. This kind of thoughts appears, on the surface, meaningless. Moreover, for many reasons it is not easy during ordinary wakeful thinking to let our thoughts drift in such a manner. This type of thinking enters, as an important element, into poetry. In fact, contemporary poetry has enriched and deepened the stream of poetic imagery precisely by this method and it is the reason why so much of it appears at first sight as a crazy-quilt. It has also quite consciously been employed in the novel, particularly by James Joyce. The apparent incoherence of those free-floating thoughts becomes suddenly meaningful when one looks at them more closely. One is able to recognize a pattern in the seemingly patternless, a grouping and coherence of a sort which is different from the logic of wakeful thinking.

These laws were discovered quite independently of Freud, by C. G. Jung at the beginning of this century. Jung's discovery consolidated the foundations of the psycho-analytic theory. The laws which seemed to govern the 'crazy' flow of freely associated thoughts—as in a completely relaxed person shortly before falling asleep—were found to be closely related to the same laws which governed the connection between symptom and unconscious conflict in conversion hysteria. In fact, it was seen that there is no such thing as 'meaningless' in the psychological order, provided that one admits the basic Freudian contention that there exists a dynamic relationship between the unconscious and the conscious. When the unconscious was no longer viewed merely as a storage-room for multiplication tables, geography, and birthday dates—the moment it became personalized, as it were—the entire distinction between meaningful and meaningless in the realm of the psychic disappeared. Particularly such manifestations of mental life as dreams and the mistakes of everyday life (forgetting, slips of the tongue, and so on) which had hitherto most frequently been regarded as senseless, suddenly 'made sense' literally.

Whoever explores the unconscious has to study that which, in the light of wakeful coherent thinking, appears absolutely or comparatively meaningless: free-floating thoughts, dreams, and the mistakes of everyday life. Actually the neurotic symptom belongs in this very order of things. It 'makes no sense' to be afraid to be alone in a room, or to be afraid of any height higher than the third floor, or to ruin one's life by drinking, or to become suspicious every time your husband has missed the bus and is ten minutes late, or to have to look ten times to see whether the gas tap in the kitchen is turned off. In other words there exist in the psychic order two sets of phenomena which are senseless in the light of logical thinking: those which are abnormal (such symptoms as I have just haphazardly enumerated) and those which are normal (free-floating thoughts, dreams, and everyday lapses).

It often happens that patients who have done no psycho-analytic reading, and who are asked to remember their dreams, come into the office for their second session and report their 'first' dream with the remark: 'It's completely crazy.' And in a certain sense they are right. Psycho-analytic studies have shown that all those 'normal' things which pass through our head when we are 'not thinking about anything in particular' and all the 'abnormal' things which are regarded as 'crazy' (the common symptoms of insane and of neurotic patients) are intrinsically connected. A study of the first set of phenomena elucidates the second set. Their coherence is different from the logical coherence of, let us say, algebra and geometry. *But that vast dark universe of the 'meaningless' which exists outside the world illuminated by logic becomes one meaningful structure once we have introduced certain tentative premises. Before we form concepts, before we think in words, and before we begin to think in logical abstractions we go through an infantile phase in which the universe of our mind consists of sensation and imagery. The connection between that preconceptual rock bottom and the upper layer of logical conceptual thinking is mysterious. But it is not unfathomable.*

This is a tremendous step forward. As we have already said, it is no exaggeration to compare this, in the history of psychology, with the Galilean revolution in the history of physics.

The next element to discuss in psycho-analytic theory is the concept of libido. To explain this better one has first to mention certain trends in the natural sciences of the nineteenth century which entered into its formation. One of these trends is characterized by the well-known law of the conservation of energy—that the total amount of energy in the universe remains exactly the same, even if the forms of energy change continuously into one another. The other trend is the theory of electro-magnetic energy as elaborated by Maxwell, which simply says that all forms of energy except gravity are, as it were, 'different expressions of the same thing.' Thus visible light, X-rays, heat, ultra-red, ultra-violet, and radio waves are *all* electro-magnetic waves. They differ from one another only by something quantitative, namely wavelengths.

Another concept which enters into the theory of libido lies outside the realm of physics. It is borrowed from a biological discipline: embryology. The embryologist studies the human form from the stage of the fertilized ovum until birth. He follows the cell division after conception, when the cells form a round compact cluster (morula), then a hollow ball with an opening (gastrula), dim ancestral phases of life through which we all pass—up to more and more differentiated arrangements of tissues and organs, until finally the human body emerges as it appears at birth. During that process the most extraordinary transmigrations occur. It is as if Nature tried things out, rejected them as not feasible, and started them all over in a new form. And these 'stabs,' these achievements by 'trial and error,' are repeated in the life, before birth, of every human being. Thus, for example, the kidneys as we know them in the human body after birth, are actually our third pair. In each human embryo Nature makes two stabs at kidney formation which are rejected as if not appropriate, so to speak, for a human body. Only the third try remains for keeps. Similarly, the gradual unfolding of the form of the heart and of the central nervous system are developments of such marvellous complexity that they represent scientific disciplines in themselves; entire libraries are devoted to the embryology of these organs. Even the uninitiated reader will readily understand that the science of embryology contributes a great deal to the understanding of the abnormal. It is obvious, for example, that the malformations with which some children are born can be understood only on the basis of embryology. Thus, the condition commonly known as hare-lip is due to the fact that two peninsulas, which form part of the upper lip of the embryo, do not fuse and remain gaping. The original morphology of the face of the human embryo presents a weird picture. Whoever sees a photograph of that stage for the first time is shocked. There are three flaps of tissue converging towards a hole, the mouth. Under normal circumstances they are later to form the upper lip with its symmetrical line swerving towards the angle of the mouth on either side and the characteristic trough which stretches from the middle of the nose straight down. The fact that in the case of a hare-lip two out of these three flaps do not fuse shows that a process has been *arrested* before its completion. This is the mechanism of many malformations. It is even the origin of certain tumours which grow in the adult body.

In other diseases it occurs that the organism reverts to forms or functions which are normal during an embryonic phase. For example, in certain diseases of the blood, there occur blood cells which under normal conditions circulate only in the embryonic blood. The same is true about certain phases of inflammatory reactions—that is to say, when the organism is in danger. Thus we see that besides arrestation at embryonic stages there occurs also a *regression* to earlier forms of life.

I have gone in detail into the theoretical elements borrowed from physics and from biology, which entered into Freud's theory of libido, because a knowledge of those elements makes this theory much more understandable. We have already seen that in the theory of the conversion symptom the human person was conceived as a universe in which no 'emotional tension' can be lost. Just as in the steam-engine heat is converted into mechanical energy, thus in a child inner conflicts and the tension associated with them may be 'converted' into hysterical convulsions.

Libido, in the original meaning, means pleasure as well as desire for pleasure. The word is used by ancient authors in either of these two meanings. In the Freudian theory all forms of pleasure are intrinsically related to one another, not unlike the way in which the various forms of electro-magnetic energy are on the basis of Clerk Maxwell's theory. Incidentally, during a later development, the concept of libido was widened so as to comprise all forms of love. Psycho-analysis does not say that the pleasure of eating, the pleasure of walking, sex pleasure and the rapture of artistic creation are all 'the same thing.' We know that they are not and no theory, no matter how clever, could convince us that they are. Nor does physics claim that light, X-rays, radio waves, and heat are all 'the same thing.' But just as Clerk Maxwell's mathematical procedure by which they were, in a sense, regarded as 'the same thing' helped us to understand an enormous mass of physical data, so Freud's procedure by which all forms of pleasure are, in a sense, regarded as 'the same thing' helps us to understand an enormous amount of psychological data.

It goes without saying, incidentally, that, despite all this, physics cannot tell us anything about the true nature of energy. The existence in the cosmos of that which is called 'energy' is elucidated through the medium of mathematical abstractions but the thing itself is as mysterious as ever. So is the existence of Desire and Pleasure in the psychological universe.

Phenomenologically, that is to say on the basis of subjective experience, all forms of pleasure differ from one another. Nevertheless, they all (whether associated with sex, or with eating, or with the experience of beauty in nature or in art, and so on) have something in common. This is also true as in the case of pain. A toothache, a pain of the shin-bone, the experience after receiving the news of the death of a beloved person—all are entirely different. Yet they all have something in common.

Now according to the psycho-analytic theory the various forms of desire and of pleasure are related to one another by a most extraordinary law of development. According to this theory, the most intense form of bodily pleasure, sexual orgasm, is ontogenetically (embryologically) related to *all* forms of bodily pleasure. (The words 'ontogenetic' and 'embryological' in this connection refer to life after birth.) It has its typical ontogenetic history. Libido, in its most archaic form, is diffusely experienced all over the body. In its earliest phase it is related to genital pleasure of the mature body as a simple, undifferentiated structure (matrix) of embryonic tissues is to the post-natal body with fully developed organs. However, even during those earlier phases, there exist areas of higher concentration, as it were. While in the infant the entire skin is erogenic, those places in which skin and mucous membranes meet—the oral, anal, and urethral area—are more so than the rest of the skin. On that archaic level it seems that the most powerful 'sense' of communication, and of relationship with the world outside the body, is through the sense of touch, and there particularly through the material exchange of matter which is not of the body—namely, food and excrement.

Even these phases—'primitive' as they appear to our abstract, adult mode of thinking—are highly significant phases of development. It could not be otherwise if one thinks of the time experience unimaginably magnified, and of 'wounds' becoming more decisive the earlier our psychic tissue is affected. It is exceedingly difficult to reconstruct such an image of ourselves and of the world in which each one of us lived at one time. Moreover, the thinking of scientifically trained people is such that, at best, such an archaic image of the world of experiences is one thing and our adult mode of thinking is another. It is hard to grasp the meaningful, organic connection between the two.

We have seen that during an early phase of life the cells form a hollow ball with a mouth-like opening. An entire class of water animals does not develop any further. The so-called cœlenterates remain for ever in the gastrula phase. A gastrula is, in the most literal sense of the word, 'all mouth.' Now, according to Freud's ontogenetic concept of the development of libido, something analogous exists in the psychic development of the infant. During the so-called first oral phase of our libidinal development we are 'all mouth,' in a passive receptive way, not unlike cœlenterates. The pleasure sensation in the oral area at the insertion of the nipple and the actual feeding is the earliest and dimmest prehistoric phase which leads up to genital sexuality. This phase is followed by the second oral phase, around the development of teeth, during which the child begins actively and aggressively to 'go out' for food, and during which part of the pleasure is not only intake but also destruction (second oral phase). The passing of fœcal material through the anal opening is associated with pleasure sensation (first anal phase). Later the child learns to retain or give fœcal material at will, and during this

D

phase (second anal phase) the retention and the 'giving' of material is associated with pleasure or with spite. These early infantile phases which are called pregenital change at a time, around the age of four, in which there occurs for the first time concentration of pleasure and desire in the genital area. This first genital phase during infancy is something which one might regard as an abortive form of puberty. It subsides during the so-called phase of 'latency' (from about the age of four to about the age of ten) which is followed by prepuberty and then puberty.

In order to outline the libido theory of neuroses in its most fundamental points one would have to add many things. For example, it is important to realize that according to this theory there is an early phase during which love knows no extraneous object. It is restricted to the immense world of the individual's own body. Moreover, at that stage the border between self and the outside world is still blurred in a way which is difficult to reconstruct for us grown-up people. The mother who is actually an object of love is still something like a huge organ-like extension of the self. The object of love is a sort of pleasure-giver, not yet exteriorized by the self, and in an archaic, 'magic' way part of the subject. 'Lust demands infinity'; this saying of Nietzsche is particularly appropriate to that earliest phase of our libidinal development. At the time when that pleasure-giving mother becomes outlined as a clear object outside ourselves our aggressive, destructive instincts are developed. And when the child realizes that the stream of love emanating from the mother is not solely directed towards himself but partly beamed at others, he wants to eliminate those competing objects. This is the time, around the 'first genital phase,' when the boy experiences the father or any other male figure as a competitor for the mother's

love. As is well known, this conflict is named Œdipus conflict after the famous Greek story of Œdipus who killed
his father and married his mother without realizing their
identity. In girls the Œdipus drama has the same powerful
impact but its plot is more complex and less well understood. Normally the Œdipus conflict is resolved by the
process of identification. During the 'latent' phase the boy
begins to pattern himself after the father, the girl after the
mother. We shall later come back to the mechanism of
identification. (In fact, several of the mechanisms outlined
here in an elementary way will be encountered again later.)
This refers also to another aspect of the psycho-analytic
theory which is closely related to the theory of libido—
that is, the organization within our unconscious of our
instinctual drives and of our forces of restraint.

The Ego—that is, our self at every second of our wakeful
existence (the 'I' which experiences and thinks)—is continuously between two energy fields, as it were. First, there
are instinctual forces which demand the fulfilment of desire
(the Id). Second, there are forces which demand restraint
and punishment (the Super-ego). These latter have originally
been extraneous but they became incorporated, and their
life within us is, curiously enough, in many ways not unlike
that of the instincts. Id and Super-ego are both for ever
pulsating at the rim of consciousness. And just as the pilot
of a plane is directed by the principle of radio pulses which
make themselves heard the moment the aeroplane deviates
from its route, the Ego, our conscious self-awareness, finds
itself under healthy circumstances in a balance between
instinctual and restraining forces. Since the Super-ego is
derived from real people, parental figures, whom we have
'internalized,' it has its own natural history in every individual. It is perhaps first always a purely inhibitory force

but then it develops also a positive function: there is a part in us which is pleased, like the benevolent parent, when we do something good. Of course, in neuroses we are usually much more concerned with the primitive or even cruel aspect of the Super-ego. This too will be more fully discussed in connection with problems pertaining to our main theme.

With reference to Freud's theory of libido, several things should be remarked at this stage of our discussion. A great number of people have a strong resistance against the idea of infantile sexuality. A theory which regards the most innocent pleasures of childhood as early forerunners of the genital pleasurc of the adult appears revolting. We frequently find behind this feeling the idea that infantile pleasure, for example of sucking, is pure while sex is 'dirty' or bad. Actually there is nothing in Christian doctrine which makes sex as such 'dirty' or bad. That there exists a first genital phase can hardly be denied on the basis of simple clinical observation. The fact that man, contrary to animals, has two puberties, an abortive one and a proper one, with a latent phase in between the two, opens up an entirely new aspect of the development of the human personality. We do not like to associate childhood with hatred and destructiveness, yet our reasoning is strangely distorted if we think of the innocent age, the age without guilt, as also the age without evil. Actually it would be an extraordinary paradox to assume that hatred and envy, fantasies of murder and destruction made their grand entry into the human personality only with the full development of reason.

Another aspect of psycho-analysis which we have to outline here briefly is the phenomenon of transference. Not long after the psycho-analytic method proper had been inaugurated, Freud was struck by a peculiar fact. During treatment the physician became an object of love and hatred. The patient's attitude towards the doctor went through phases of an intense emotional colouring. These phases were mysterious. They could not, like ordinary love and hatred, be explained by the actual situation. The mystery was solved when it was found that in such a setting the physician was not a neutral figure but represented, under disguise, a powerful figure from the patient's infantile background. Usually he was a parental figure, a father or a mother, or a sibling figure, a brother or sister. The love or hatred experienced during the treatment was not directed towards the analyst, but towards someone else in whose place he stood. The patient was not aware of this. But when it was interpreted to him at the proper moment he learned to realize something which is so highly important to us if we want to understand ourselves; namely, that all our emotional relationships are tainted by a carry-over. That which determines our earliest relationships— the original 'plot' which is played between ourselves and those huge over-lifesize *dramatis personæ* of the family— has an impact on all the later dramas of life. We paraphrase it, we vary it a bit, but what we really want to do is to play it over and over again. And the reason why so many things go mysteriously wrong between ourselves and people around us, at school, at work, in marriage, is that we repeat performances of a play which was actually, in every single case, unique.

This carrying over of unfinished business, let us say from the relationship 'son-father' to the relationship 'patient-doctor,' is called transference. A great deal of analytical treatment consists of interpreting again and again this transference to the patient until the gap between infantile fantasy and objective reality gradually widens. This, in fact, is the aim of all psycho-analytical therapy. It is not an exaggeration to say that the patient is well when he is able to encounter people in his everyday environment without endowing them with qualities which are borrowed from the persons who populated the primeval stage.

There is one more psycho-analytical concept which has to be briefly explained in order to make the following discussions clearer—the concept of sublimation. The word 'sublimation' is borrowed from chemistry. There it means the changing of a substance from its solid to its gaseous state, without passing first through the liquid state. In psycho-analysis it means the transformation of instinctual drives into forms of human energy on a more elevated level.

This concept existed, in various aspects, long before Freud. For example, it was a rule during antiquity that athletes should remain sexually abstinent before some sports event; this ascetic practice would enhance their athletic prowess. Several famous artists have stated that sexual abstinence increased their creativeness. All this, contrary to the psycho-analytic concept, refers to the *conscious* level. Like some other psycho-analytic concepts, the idea of sublimation was anticipated by nineteenth-century German philosophy—this one particularly by Schopenhauer. In psycho-analytic theory, due to the ideas of quantities of energy and so on, the concept of sublimation has a strongly mechanistic flavour. But it corresponds to an obvious fact just the same, and one can readily see why it should play a great role in neuroses and their therapy.

In connection with the concept of sublimation, we can anticipate something which will later be elaborated.

The idea of sublimation shows clearly that something mechanistic, a 'process' analogous to a chemical one, an image borrowed from the test-tube, is poorly deficient in comparison with the thing for which it stands. Actually it has vast implications. For example, suppose I could show that a headmaster of a school who is an outstanding educator has 'sublimated' his 'latent homosexuality' in his work. In this case I would demonstrate something for which all clinical terms are primitive symbols. I would actually, without realizing it, be touching upon something of the ontological order—at any rate something which is beyond the clinical and the psychological. This is a thread which we shall have to pick up again at another phase of this discussion.

# VI     The Third Revolution

> It is simply incomprehensible how anybody can consider the Christian doctrine of redemption as a guide for the difficult life of today.
> <div align="right">JOSEPH GOEBBELS, <i>Diaries</i></div>

> Only that which is replaced, is destroyed.
> AUGUSTE COMTE

THE things which have been explained in the preceding chapter may be true or not. But the question whether they are true or not is not a philosophical problem. To dispute the basic tenets of psycho-analysis on philosophical grounds would be just as wrong as to dispute certain tenets of physics on philosophical grounds. All we can say is that nothing discussed in the preceding chapter is incompatible with a Christian idea of the nature of man. On the contrary, we shall see that these tenets fit in perfectly with such an idea. If the tenets are, as we think, empirically established, there is no paradox. Anything true is part of Truth itself.

It is therefore the more surprising that psycho-analysis is considered a vicious onslaught against Christianity, in fact against any religious belief. There are two main reasons for this which we have to discuss separately. First, Freud did not stop at factual statements to which the tests of veracity can be applied. He ventured into philosophy and expounded his ideas on religion. Second, Freud's psychological concepts, by a strange historical development, fused with many of the scientific concepts of the nineteenth century. Sciences which, from the point of view of method, are quite opposed to one another, form strange combinations. Psycho-analysis has been confirmed, in parts, by brain physiology; the social sciences have borrowed working concepts from psycho-analysis, and so on. All this is well and good. But it means that certain distinctions which are very important to the clarification of our present thesis have become blurred. When one is dealing with hybrids, it is hard to get a clear idea of basic premises.

Philosophy itself has a unifying power. Just as all people who believe in the Divinity of Christ and the work of the Redemption are united by certain basic concepts, people who have abandoned their belief in the supernatural are united by other basic concepts. Thus, all sciences pertaining to Man have a tendency to coalesce into a sort of body which is entirely separate from a Christian anthropology.

Let us first discuss Freud's philosophy of religion and then certain present-day trends with which it falls in. Freud himself has written several essays on religion; there are numerous papers on this subject by his pupils. We cannot discuss Freud's views on religion in as great detail as we should like, but this has been done by several writers.[1] The general nature of Freud's views on religion can be summarized in two points.

First, Freud's method in dealing with anything spiritual is *reductive*. This means that Freud reduces everything which, to the religious believer, is in the supernatural order, to something in the natural order. For example, the idea of

[1] B. G. Sanders, *Christianity after Freud*, London, 1949, in which the author brings out several illuminating details. Also Roland Dalbiez, Psycho-analytic Method and the Doctrine of Freud (London, 1941).

God, says Freud, is a father image projected on the sky. The child originally has a concept of an omnipotent father who is able to fulfil all his needs. In the degree to which the child develops a grasp of reality, that image of the father is gradually erased. Instead of it, a fantasy figure, a father in heaven, becomes imbued with the same qualities of omnipotence and protectiveness.

To take another example, Freud would say that the idea of Holy Communion is derived from the primitive state (or childhood) of mankind, when the rite of oral incorporation of the father, in cannibalistic or sacrificial ceremonies, was common.

In other words, God is *nothing but* the father and Holy Communion is *nothing but* cannibalistic oral introjection. In fact, anything in the spiritual order is 'nothing but.' This is quite logical for Freud. If one denies the existence of things beyond the natural, the only possible conclusion is a philosophy of 'nothing but,' a philosophy of debunking. This is common to all materialist trends of the nineteenth century, indeed to all schools of thought which look on nature as something outside a Christo-centric sphere. To a modern astronomer the earth is *nothing but* an insignificant speck in the galaxy; to the biologist man is *nothing but* some chance product of an evolutional process which has no transcendental meaning; to a dialectical materialist cultural achievements are *nothing but* by-products of the economic struggle.

This theory of 'nothing but' appears the more devastating the more it advances towards things of a psychic nature. This is why the 'nothing but' of Freud appears more threatening to the faithful Christian than, let us say, the 'nothing but' of the post-Copernican astronomer. Actually, in principle it is the same thing. Only with the Freudian reductive philosophy the opposing fronts are drawn up much more clearly than before. The 'nothing but' of Freud is the complete inversion, the upside-down, the perfect mirror image of the Christian position. Whereas Freud tells us that God is nothing but a father figure, or that the idea of the Eucharist is nothing but oral introjection, a Christian philosopher would say: 'Even in the child's relationship to the father, there is contained a crude fore-shadowing of our relationship to God,' or 'Even in the earliest sacrificial rituals, there is contained a crude fore-shadowing of the idea of Holy Communion,' and so on. Saint Paul speaks in these terms quite explicitly: 'God, after Whom all fatherhood on earth is named' (Eph. iii. 15). The situation is similar to certain law-suits in which two testimonies are given which contradict each other com-pletely. Here for once it is quite impossible that both parties are right. Contrary to the history of other clashes between science and religion, in this case a compromise or a settlement out of court will not do.

The most remarkable of all the reductive statements is this: Religion is nothing but an obsessive-compulsive neurosis. This brings us to our second point, the historical theories of religion which Freud developed in various papers and which the reader can study in detail in the author's original works. A compulsive-obsessive neurosis is a state in which the patient sees himself forced to go through apparently irrational acts. He may have to wash his hands a certain number of times in situations in which hand-washing is actually not warranted; he may have to touch certain objects; he may have to avoid the touching of other objects; he may have to avoid certain steps on the stair-case or repeat certain other steps a given number of times, and so on. There is something 'ritualistic' about many of these compulsive-obsessive acts. For example, some of them are carried out before going to bed, and unless they are carried out the patient cannot sleep in peace. Moreover, these acts usually have no practical meaning, and when they are carried out repeatedly one can sometimes observe a preference for 'magic' numbers, such as three or seven. It occurred to Freud quite early in the course of his studies that all great religions appear like obsessive-compulsive mechanisms on a large scale—transposed into mass psychology, as it were. From this he concluded that religion *is* a compulsive-obsessive neurosis. Indeed, the liturgical ritual and the ascetic ideal, two elements which all the great religions of the world have in common, bear a striking resemblance to the compulsive symptoms of neuroses. There are certain individuals in whom even the inner experience accompanying religious activities is similar to that encountered in compulsive neurotics.

It is characteristic of compulsive-obsessive patients that in early childhood, before the latent phase, a trauma or a set of traumas occurred. This trauma is associated with guilt. The obsessive thought or the compulsive act of the patient can be shown to represent an unconscious re-enactment of the traumatic experience, or an unconscious act of penance—a ritual to ward off punishment threatening from without. Almost all children, for example, have compulsive tendencies during pre-puberty. These unconsciously self-imposed rituals of penance have something to do with the reawakening of the sexual instinct during the second genital phase, which brings with it a reawakening of preconceptual infantile feeling of guilt.

In studying the phenomena of religious practice, Freud came to the conclusion that there must exist an analogy in the history of mankind. In a dim faraway prehistoric phase, some horrible offence must have been committed. When man lived through his early infancy, in a social structure which is best described as 'the horde of sons,' the Big Crime, the killing of the father, was carried out. All ideas of sacrifice, particularly all sacrificial rites, can be explained on this basis. In his papers on religion, particularly in *Moses and Monotheism*, Freud elaborated this hypothesis in sweeping, daring lines to give a psycho-analytic interpretation of the origin of Judaism and Christianity (which he conceived as a logical development of Judaism).

A factual criticism of this theory has been made by others, and therefore should not be repeated here. Considering that all this was written by an atheist of the nineteenth century, the reader must be struck by something else. This is not quite the language and the thought of the typical 'debunking' scientist. A logical positivist could not have painted such a tableau. To him the idea of reconstructing the story of a primeval horde of sons, of the Great Patricide by which something like collective guilt came into the world, must appear mad. It is not quite the language of science. If one compares this story with the writings on religion from the time of the Enlightenment, one feels indeed that something new has been added. Anyone who has read the typical anti-religious pamphlets by nineteenth-century scientists cannot help feeling that there is in Freud's writings on religion too much of the other nineteenth century, the century of Kierkegaard and Nietzsche, the century of spiritual restlessness. That entire story of the one horrid transgression which, after millenniums of 'latency,' brings the origin of 'religion' about, is (quite irrespective of its merits with regard to truth or falsity) somehow not the proper thing for a scientific atheist. Mr Popper would undoubtedly detect a metaphysical scent in it.

As Sanders in his critical study has already pointed out, there is actually nothing in Freud's analysis which would explain why the sons felt guilty at all after killing the father, and why such collective guilt would establish itself once and for all in the hearts of men. There is nothing on the psychological plane which would account for such a strange story of inheritance. There are remarkable points of resemblance with the Christian version, the story of the Fall. 'Paul, a Roman Jew from Tarsus, seizes upon this feeling of guilt and correctly traced it back to its primeval source.'[1] It is remarkable that Freud should use the word 'correctly.' If a modern scientist, without any faith in the supernatural, without any acknowledgement of that which is of the order of Grace, set out to debunk religion and produced his own home-made theology—this is just about as close to the world of revelation as he possibly could come.

There are two big schools of anti-Christian philosophy in the world today: dialectical materialism in Russia and scientific positivism outside Russia. Freud's anti-religious writings do not fit into either of them. They are not quite rationalistic enough. They are odd. They emphasize too much an element of tragedy. And it is most characteristic of all scientific materialism (whether of the Russian or of the Western variety) that it denies tragedy. Its solutions are simple and pat. Therefore we should not be surprised that Freud's papers dealing with the historical origin of monotheism have not had a profound influence on the reading public as a whole. They have created nothing in the popular mind like the wave following the post-Darwinian evolutionist literature; there is nothing in these writings to 'catch on.'

It is quite easy to disprove Freud's theory on its own

[1] Freud, *Moses and Monotheism.*

terms. One does not even need to bring in theology. The argument is flimsy, regardless of what one's faith or lack of faith may be. If one accepts Freud's theory of the development of libido, one thing (e.g., the Eucharist) cannot *be* another thing (primeval cannibalistic ritual). The relationship is quite different. Supposing you were enthralled by the beauty of the face of Michelangelo's 'David,' and I opened a text-book of human embryology and showed you a picture with bulb-like eye buds, a gaping slit for a mouth, and the arches of gills underneath. You might say: 'Isn't it marvellous how the human face can develop out of that form!' Or: 'How mysterious! Why do we all have to pass through this stage? If nature meant us to have a face, why not just have one?' These remarks would be justified. But if I tried to destroy your enthusiasm by saying: 'My dear man, David's face is *nothing but* two bulb-like buds, a slit, and arches of gills underneath,' you would doubt whether I was in my right mind. And quite rightly so, because the one thing just *is not* the other. What is more, in order to understand the form and beauty of the face of 'David,' we do not need to know anything about embryology. As a matter of fact, that knowledge might even detract, if anything, from the æsthetic enjoyment.

It is important to realize that the 'nothing but' philosophy contains in addition a grain of Manichæan hatred of nature. When a man says that a rose is nothing but humus and manure (because this is the stuff out of which it grows), he is not only wrong: he also implies that the rose cannot be such a beautiful form as all that because it is made up of something which is 'not nice.' This element is common to all debunking philosophies. A very common debunking formula is contained in this thought expressed by Mr Popper: 'It is well known that the terminology of mysticism, the mystical union, the mystical intuition of beauty, mystical love, have in all times been borrowed from the realm of relations between individual men, and especially from the experience of sexual love. . . .' This is true. It is generally accepted that the *Song of Songs* refers to human love and to mystical union at the same time. One can interpret it either way. But Popper's objection[1] not only means that mysticism is nonsense because it cannot be formulated scientifically; it also means that mysticism must be nonsense because its terminology is borrowed from something 'low.' There is in the 'nothing but' or debunking approach a subtle, hidden contempt for the flesh, a hatred of nature. The psycho-analyst turned philosopher is just like the positivist, a disguised half-brother of the Puritan.

The fallacy has still another aspect—the over-extension of the psychological method, beyond the domain of psychology. If someone decides, merely on the basis of psychological observation, what God is, what Holy Communion is, what Mystical Union is—then there is no boundary to psychology. This would mean that psychology can answer all problems, and that things have no true essence.

Many modern thinkers who took a destructive line, from Nietzsche to Jean-Paul Sartre, have succumbed to this fallacy. The same thing can be said about the observations on 'religion' by representatives of the so-called cultural psycho-analytical schools who are believed to have rejected Freud's materialism. It is most remarkable that Husserl, just around the beginning of this century, and apparently without being aware of the beginnings made by Freud, warned of the danger of what he called *psychologism*. Little

[1] Mr Popper's argument has, of course, nothing whatever to do with psycho-analysis; it is the principle behind his argument which interests us.

did he realize the disastrous social implications of all
this.

Like all materialist philosophies the Freudian, too, contains inner contradictions, certain idealist[1] elements in
disguise. For example, if one really believed wholeheartedly
in the primacy of blind instinctual drives and determina-
tion by the irrational, the entire idea of sublimation would
make no sense. Freud has indicated time and time again
that sublimation is the ideal solution of the neurotic conflict; Thomas Mann says that this alone puts him in line
with the great humanists. But this means the introduction
of a moral principle which is not intrinsic to the system.
As we have already pointed out, in psycho-analytical literature sublimation is usually described in mechanistic terms.
Since instincts, if they were freely expressed, would clash
with social taboos, they are channelled into something else.
Actually nobody really believes in such a crude machinery.
The very formation of the concept of sublimation implies
the existence of something beyond it. Does anyone really
believe that families are founded, orphans are cared for,
the sick are tended to, cathedrals are erected, symphonies
are composed—only because instinctual drives are blocked
by society? The adherence to the 'machinery' when it
comes to these questions is due to the fear which all authors
of mechanistic systems have of the idea of finality. Even if
one accepted the mechanistic concept to that extent, the
question would still have to be answered as to why 'society'
began to inhibit instinctual drives in the first place.

There is a resemblance between this paradox and the
famous one in which the Marxists are involved. If one took

---

[1] The word 'idealist' is not meant in the technical sense of a definite
philosophical school but generally as indicating the opposite of 'materialist.'

the Marxist philosophy literally, it would be nonsense to go to prison for it, to face Siberia or a firing squad, to endure hunger and sickness, or to do anything at all so that later generations, after our death, should live in a society in which justice reigns. Yet this was the moral philosophy of many early Marxist revolutionaries.

It has frequently been pointed out that in Marx's philosophy of history, with the proletariat, the down-trodden class, in the role of a saviour—there is something like a prophetic and messianic afterthought, not at all in step with dialectics. There is something similar the matter with Freud's theory as to how religion came about. As we have seen, it bears strange resemblances to the Christian 'myth' itself. With all its distortions, it is derived from somewhere beyond the biological diagrams.

In view of the oddity of Freud's books on religion, their subtlety and complexity, their hidden element of tragedy which removes them from the category of popular literature, we must ask ourselves: How can those ideas possibly find an expression in the social structure? How can they shape the outlook and the philosophy of the common man in the way in which the post-Darwinian evolutionist ideas did?

There are various reasons for apprehension about the effect of these ideas. First, the philosophy of 'nothing but' —of reduction—is the most widely accepted psycho-analytic tenet. This has really penetrated popular thought, in contrast to Freud's historical theory of Judaeo-Christianity. It is most harmoniously in step with a general phase of moral and spiritual devaluation. There are a great many people with university education who have only an imperfect knowledge of what psycho-analysis is really about, yet the 'nothing but' philosophy expresses clearly what they have been somehow aware of all the time. Even if they would not go the whole way about libido or the nature of the unconscious, they would readily admit that God is nothing but a glorified father image, and that the Church is certainly only a mother image, a womb. This movement of devaluation is happening on a considerable social scale.

In addition to the regular body of knowledge which is part of our education and culture, there is a second body, the Encyclopædia of Better-Knowing. Not only do we know things; we are at the same time 'enlightened' about them. This phenomenon is part of a movement which might be called the Inverted Renaissance. During the Renaissance, as everybody knows, philosophers and theologians intruded in matters which were strictly of the scientific order. Whatever the historical details may have been in the famous case of Galileo, science did not benefit from such a theological intrusion at the beginning of modern times. There is no reason why philosophers and theologians, who deal with things of the metaphysical order, should become involved with such questions as the number of teeth in a horse's mouth, or the elliptic curves of stellar movements. The dreadful mistake was made and very soon the opposite process got under way; today we are at the height of the reaction. Today science takes its revenge for what happened four hundred years ago. There are continuous forays and occasional invasions into the domain of metaphysics. The results are always disastrous.

This can be best demonstrated by the case of Darwin. It sounds incredible, but there is a direct line leading from Darwin to Hitler. It seems grotesque to link up the innocent passenger of the good ship *Beagle*, one of the finest examples of what a scientist should be, with the concentration camps of Belsen and Buchenwald. Yet the fact remains that there is a link. Darwin's theory of the survival of the fittest has to be judged on its own merits, as a scientific hypothesis. It referred to animals, not to men. But it contributed, quite independently of the intentions of its originator, to something which one might call the climate of our times. The beginning was harmless enough: pamphlets were tossed from rectories into laboratories and back. However, it was not long before men like the German Nietzsche and the Frenchman Gobineau appeared on the scene. These men thought that it might not be such a bad idea for society if the stronger ones stepped on their less well-endowed brethren—meaning human beings. Even at that stage there was something academic and, in a sense, aristocratic about the entire affair. If one had known one of those thinkers personally he would undoubtedly have said: 'They talk like that, but they don't really mean it.' It took another generation for this thought to have any influence on the lives of people, and it finally 'made history.'

Several things had to happen to achieve this success. This philosophy agglutinated with other similar trends. There was Wagner's and Schopenhauer's irrational 'death magic'; there existed a political philosophy of strength and superiority; there followed the political and social setting of Central Europe in the era following the First World War; and certain personalities (who are always ready to make a mass distribution of ideas in a cheap edition) appeared on the scene. In other words, it took three generations for a new scientific concept to have its full impact on the world of values. An element of the natural order, the biological nature of Man, was elevated to a position of primacy. Three generations later the human image was distorted beyond recognition.

Unlike Darwin, and in this respect more like Freud, Karl Marx supplied his own philosophical superstructure for the theory of economic determinism. Actually, Marx also began with a 'nothing but' theory. The questions of whether there exists such a thing as surplus value, and whether things of the spirit are really nothing but accidental by-products of what happens on the economic plane, are really quite academic. *Das Kapital* is a book of the same kind as *The Origin of Species*, except perhaps that it is drier and less readable. In the case of this 'reductive' theory, too, it took three generations, and a similar mechanism of agglutination and vulgarization, until the finished product was achieved in our century. The important point is that here, too, something of the natural order was elevated to a position of primacy over the spirit. The result has been a most fiendish form of dehumanization, something like a preternatural spectacle in which the human form can no longer be discerned. I agree with those who believe that the prophet himself would not recognize his product today. After all, Marx with all his hostility against the existing order, with all the blustering jargon and furious invective, seems primarily to have been moved by a human feeling for social justice and a human dissatisfaction with the ills of the early period of industrialization. This moral motivation got completely lost in the historical development.

The unspeakable things which happened when the biological was allotted a position of primacy in Germany, and when the economic was allotted a position of primacy in Russia, should give us a fair warning. 'A man will reap what he sows; if nature is his seed-ground, nature will give him a perishable harvest; if his seed-ground is the spirit, it will give him a harvest of eternal life' (St Paul, Epistle to the Gal. vi, 8[1]).

*          *          *

[1] Knox translation.

The 'nothing but' which is the core of Freudian philosophy is bound to have an impact no less formidable. One cannot just say these things in an atmosphere of academic neutrality. The situation is precisely the same as in the two other 'revolutions.' The entire philosophical superstructure which the creator of psycho-analysis delivered, together with his discovery, was not much more than an academic play. Despite all the fun Freud made of the 'moralists,' he himself was a man of great moral nobility. There are numerous facts about his own life to substantiate this. It is the same theoretical paradox which one encounters in so many of the early dialectical materialists.

However, the psychological revolution has already sped far past the aristocratic and esoteric stages; it has entered the phase of vulgarization. The philosophical utterances of the second and third echelons lack the lonely and tragic element of the original theorists. They are related to Freud as some of the German and Austrian experts on the philosophy of the race were to Nietzsche and Gobineau. What is even more remarkable, the process of agglutination which we have seen in the development of the biological revolt is quite advanced. We have seen that behaviourism and the reflexology of Pavlov were originally quite opposed to psycho-analysis. They discard the empathic-intuitive element in psychology as unscientific. They accept only the *homme machine* of Descartes, the mechanistic model, as the last image of truth beyond which there is nothing. So does the cybernetics man turned psychiatrist. In so far as Freud introduced the terminology of the 'model' (the 'quantum' of libidinal energy which is shunted back and forth), he had outwardly assimilated his system to that of the *homme machine*. This is one of the reasons why he is a determinist and regards the idea of free will as an illusion.

Moreover, as we have seen, there are large areas in the social sciences in which, for the purpose of scientific enquiry, numbers of people in their relationships to one another are treated under the fictitious premise of a *mechanism*. The same is true about large sectors of anthropology and comparative sociology. In other words, the psycho-analytic movement has *fused* with a body of the most divergent kinds of science which deal with human problems.

It is a huge body of synthesis, of cross-breeding in which psycho-analysis as such, the art of the healing dialogue, can no longer be recognized. What interests us most is the fact that those sciences can be used for managerial purposes; they can easily be employed as a tool for the manipulation of great numbers of human beings. Moreover, they have an imponderable but vast influence on the common sense of values. As far as the first feature is concerned one is able, even now, to discern signs of things to come. It is little realized to what extent behaviouristic and psycho-analytical knowledge is already being used for managerial purposes.[1]

The beginnings look harmless to the superficial observer. An American company wanted to know why people chew gum. An advertising agency which employs psychologists undertook the task of research. They produced three reasons for gum chewing—'for oral comfort, for release of tension, to express symbolic hostility and aggression.' The advertising agency next made a comprehensive sociological survey 'of a coal-mining area in eastern Pennsylvania, where gum sales were well below the national level.' Mr Goodman states:

It discovered that the area had a relatively high rate of illiteracy, a large foreign-born population, and a low standard

[1] For details, see Ralph Goodman, 'Freud and the Hucksters,' *The Nation*, CLXXVI, 143–145, 1953.

of living. Putting the results of the two studies together, the agency laid out a campaign for this particular region. The theme was frustration and the relief obtained by chewing gum. The idea was presented in a series of comic-strip ads. The first showed a child unable to do a simple, everyday task and overcoming his difficulty after an adult gave him a stick of gum. A second showed adults conquering frustration in the same way. The strips used a minimum of words so as to avoid the impression of insincerity and reach a not too literate public.

The firm reported that sales in the test area increased at a much higher rate than in the rest of the country during the year that the campaign ran. As a result the campaign was expanded to fourteen other markets. After quoting startling examples to show how outstanding social psychologists who have earned considerable scientific reputation go in for this sort of thing, the author observes:

> Social scientists in the past have paid attention to the irrational patterns of human behaviour because they wish to locate their social origins and thus be able to suggest changes that would result in more rational conduct. They now study irrationality—and other aspects of human behaviour—to gather data that may be used by salesmen to manipulate consumers. No one can believe that chewing gum will relieve the basic frustrations of Pennsylvania coal miners.

The author shows how the same science is used in other 'markets,' less irrelevant than chewing gum, including the psychology of political influence. It does not take much imagination to expand all this into the science of an Orwellian society.

Apart from the danger of a tool for mass manipulation and social engineering, there is the general climate which these sciences create. They work more or less on the basis of a creed, which is this: values, particularly moral ones, are non-transcendental, and lie on the same plane as the social, economic, and psychological function investigated; they are contingent on, and a product of, social, economic, and psychological data which themselves are arbitrary and shifting.

I say 'more or less' because there is a small number of persons who are stricken with doubts. It is the general atmosphere which counts. One could call this the materialism of the better classes. Anyone engaged in empirical work is entitled to put in an appearance as a philosopher. It is in this 'philosophy' that the strangest bedfellows, such as the behaviourist and the psycho-analyst, meet. It has the unifying power of faith. To observe this one can open any scholarly journal or manual in those fields practically at random. The element which is perhaps more than anything else reminiscent of the hatching period of nihilism is that ubiquitousness, certainty, and peculiar touch of banality which is so difficult to define—a characteristic sort of *petit bourgeois* mediocrity which is associated with a contempt for the spirit.

If anyone had attempted in the late 'twenties to make a forecast about the future cultural climate of Germany, he would have followed a completely wrong track in studying Husserl or Scheler or Jaspers. What he should have done was to study the philosophical utterances of dozens of obscure professors of anthropology, political science, and so on. Today, if we take philosophy from the mere point of view of the prognostic symptom, it might be quite wrong to pick the writings of, say, Mr Niebuhr. The philosopher seems at times as detached from the main current as the artist. Therefore, if we want to study

*Weltanschauung* as a *symptom* we have to go to other sources. It is the philosophy of the technicians which provides the index.

Mr Kinsey, a zoologist who earned his original scientific reputation by his work on the gall wasp, does not mince words when he speaks of the moral values of man: 'The mores, whether they concern food, clothing, sex or religious rituals, originate neither in accumulated experience nor in scientific examinations of objectively gathered data. The sociologist and anthropologist find the origins of such customs in ignorance and superstition, and in the attempt of each group to set itself apart from its neighbours.'[1] Theodore Schroeder,[2] a psycho-analyst, came to the same conclusion earlier and quite independently: 'The evil of all morals lies in their subjective and "unconscious" sources; in their immature or morbid sentimentalisms, rather than in the resulting moral dogmas.'

One can see that Schroeder is emotionally less detached than Kinsey. He feels more passionate about the subject, perhaps because he has seen more of what happens to people who cling to moral laws. This may be the reason for his bitterness: 'Every variety of "split personality" (or moralist) must see human conduct and human situations through conflicting feelings. . . .' After thousands of years of what Kinsey brands as ignorance and superstition, it is not easy to formulate a revolutionary ideal so that the ordinary reader understands it. Thus Schroeder finds a formulation which cannot be immediately clear to everybody: 'The amoralist's new standard of values is a measuring of the influence of any conduct or creed, in accelerating or retarding the psycho-evolutionary processes.' In case the

[1] *Sexual Behaviour in the Human Male.* W. B. Saunders Co., 1948.
[2] Theodore Schroeder, 'Attitude of an Amoral Psychologist,' *Psychoanalytic Review*, XXXI, 329–335, 1944.

reader is misled into believing that this programme may settle the huge problem only tentatively or in part, the author is quick to add: 'That is an amoralist's substitute for *all* moral standards and judgments.' The same author had already attempted to formulate a new approach which would once and for all do away with what we have been taught at grandmother's knees. This formulation is not more propitious than the other, but since it is characteristic of a widely adopted jargon it should be given here:

> Everywhere 'education' is subordinated to religio-moralistic sentimentalism, and therefore by the psychological imperatives which make for the perpetration of infantile impulses and intellectual methods. These imperatives include the religious temperament and its anti-scientific method for promoting social progress; and for the promulgation of the morally approved emotional and ideological symptoms of the 'split personality.'
> Instead of education by moralistic or idealistic indoctrination we substitute an amoral education for mental maturing. . . . Thus we produce a realistic peace of mind which can be enjoyed only by well-unified personalities, who know how to live in harmony with the natural laws of psycho-social relations. This peace of mind must be distinguished from many popular delusions of peace. . . .[1]

In order that the reader should not consider this a mere restatement of the position of many other psycho-analysts, perhaps also to set off its radical formulation properly, this paper is entitled: 'Really New Education for Social Living.' In contrast to these dim views, expounded by a behaviourist and a psycho-analyst, there are others who are more optimistic. It is the optimism of psychological progress of which we spoke. The human heart in its relation-

[1] Theodore Schroeder, 'Really New Education for Social Living,' *Psycho-analytic Review*, XXVIII, 363–371, 1941.

ship to other men and to God is treated as if psychological mechanisms and concepts were the final formula. This trend is even more startling than the pathos of Dr Schroeder. It represents an attitude of quasi-objectivity which acknowledges moral values but makes them subject to the test of science and technique. This is extremely widespread. An entire book could be written about this phenomenon alone. But one haphazard example will suffice. A sociologist in a paper on 'Love'[1] states:

> Sullivan's definition is a helpful beginning: 'When the satisfaction or the security of another person becomes as significant to one as is one's own satisfaction or security, then the state of love exists.' But his approximation is static, unilateral, and still tinged with the Christian morality which honours sacrifice of oneself to another as an ultimate good, though it may thwart the development of both. Erich Fromm's notion of productive love, and his insistence upon the legitimacy of self-love, appear more analytically precise and valid: '. . . Love is an activity and not a passion . . . the essence of love is to "labour" for something and "to make something grow." . . . To love a person productively implies to care and to feel responsible for his life, not only for his physical existence but for the growth and development of all his human powers . . . without respect for and knowledge of the beloved person, love deteriorates into domination and possessiveness.'

This is a fairly representative sample. *Agape* is being investigated in its mechanics, under the premise that the natural plane represents the whole. It is measured against the views of two social psychologists who have come to different results, as in the good old days when pathology professors used to dispute the definition of 'inflammation.' The charity of Christ does not quite make the grade. The

[1] Nelson N. Foote, 'Love,' *Psychiatry*, XVI, 245–251, 1953.

point is not that 'Christian morality' is here represented in a perfectly distorted way. The remarkable thing is how one investigator's definition is discarded *because* it is 'still tinged' with Christian morality. There is a peculiar equating of that which lies in the order of psychological and social mechanics with that which is of the transcendental order. Gethsemane, which is a mystery, is treated as if it were a proposition. Saint John of the Cross, Saint Francis of Assisi, and Our Lord Himself become, as it were, subjects of a sociological investigation on 'personality interaction' or something of that sort. What makes all this so hideous is not so much the factual error; it is something which is perhaps best described as *a loss of the metaphysical sense.* One author, under the much more cheerful title 'Towards a Science of Morality,'[1] outlines his basic approach as follows:

> The key to a science of morality may be found in a remark made by Sigmund Freud to the effect that, rather than ask about the purpose of life, we should ask about the purposes for which men live. The fact of the matter is that men do have purposes and that, from the viewpoint of these purposes, actions are not indifferent. Some actions result in the purposes which instigate them: these actions are *good.* Some actions have consequences which interfere with the attainment of certain ends: these actions are *bad.*

In the history of spiritual landslides, there always comes a moment which is characterized by the search for the simple formula. The word of God, as revealed in its simplicity in the Ten Commandments or the Sermon on the Mount, is related to the preceding quotations as food is to synthetic chemicals. The life in Christ Crucified which is still the life of many unknown people who pass one every

[1] Isidor Chein, 'Towards a Science of Morality,' *Journal of Social Psychology*, XXV, 235–238, 1947.

day on the street is of such immediacy that we cannot imagine how it can be replaced by 'recent findings.'

It is only on the basis of the search for the simple formula that we can explain the statements of authors who advocate a radical and deep-reaching approach. Such statements are associated with an air of impatience and urgency. Dr Chisholm,[1] in his famous address on 'the re-establishment of a peace-time society,' associated in a sweeping line the eternal recurrence of wars with the existence of moral standards. Dr Chisholm's proposals for an enduring peace are daring and visionary. He insists on security through the elimination of the occasion for valid fear of aggression. This could come about by legislation backed by immediately available combined force prepared to suppress ruthlessly any appeal to force by any peoples of the world.' Secondly, he advocates an 'opportunity to live reasonably comfortable. . . .' Thirdly, and this is the most remarkable part of his dissertation, he insists on 'an elimination of neurosis,' and this is the main part of his speech. In order to eliminate neurosis (so that peace can be preserved) we must look for its cause in the world in which we live:

> The re-interpretation and eventually eradication of the concept of right and wrong which has been the basis of child training [says Dr Chisholm], the substitution of intelligent and rational thinking for faith in the certainties of the old people, these are the belated objectives of all psycho-therapy. Would they not be legitimate objectives of original education?

Dr Chisholm feels that we have no time to lose. Another world catastrophe may be imminent. Therefore quick action is needed, and although he is far from having found the

[1] G. B. Chisholm, 'The Re-establishment of a Peace-time Society,' *Psychiatry*, IX, 3–11, 1946.

entire solution for the formidable problem he has at least
a preliminary suggestion.

> Can such a programme of re-education or of a new kind
> of education be charted? I would not presume to go so far,
> except to suggest that psychology and sociology and simple
> psycho-pathology, the sciences of living, should be made
> available to all the people by being taught to all children
> in primary and secondary schools, while the study of such
> things as trigonometry, Latin, religions and others of
> specialist concern should be left to universities.

A speaker in the discussion commented on the paper
with the following remarkable words: 'It is precisely the
purpose of psychiatry to discover in a scientific way the
wellsprings of human nature even as those who are working in the religious field have endeavoured to find those
wellsprings in an authoritarian way from the Book, from
the Bible, from tradition. I will not, in order to maintain the
protective coloration, indicate where General Chisholm
thinks this feeling (a sense of inferiority and guilt and fear)
originated. I am sure we should not betray that secret.
Suffice it to say, however, that I would that this address
were mailed to all the ministers and priests in the United
States.'

We would not have quoted those papers from authors
in completely different fields if they were not representative of a great number of those engaged in the social sciences.
These things are perhaps not always expressed with the
same fervour. They certainly are not literally adhered to in
the private lives of those who pronounce them. The few
people quoted here express bluntly what hundreds of others
assume more or less without formulating it. For many
intellectuals in pre-Hitler Germany it was the smart thing

to believe in the primacy of the biological. For the charm-
ing people who populate Chekhov's stage it was the smart
thing to be nihilistic. They never bothered to think this
thought 'through' so that they might be able to behold the
end, the potential result, the concrete precipitate. They
were not able to imagine their own persons in a world in
which this thought was part of the fabric of a lived reality.
It is strange that some people can think of dehumanization
only in terms of Stalin, others only in terms of Hitler. To
many the democratic procedure itself has become something like a rite of protection. A glance at history shows
that evil never puts in an appearance twice under the same
guise.

Of course there is no war between Christianity and
paganism, as there has been in Russia and Germany, but
there are continuous border incidents, and counted up they
may amount to a war. Perhaps a state of war exists and
we do not realize it. In modern times formal declarations
of war are no longer necessary. Under the Comtean idea
of a science of man, disciplines which methodologically do
not necessarily fit together, such as psycho-analysis and
behaviourism, anthropology and psychology, psychiatry
and sociology, form a kind of unified structure. They are
held together by a common philosophical basis. They are
beginning to form a sort of Corpus Non-Mysticum. The
fulfilment of Auguste Comte's dream of a world dominated
by science is not far off.

Psycho-analysis is so strongly embedded in all this that
it is difficult to recognize its basic features. Many Christian
critics of psycho-analysis are evidently handicapped by the
thought that one has to accept all the tenets. Moreover,
they cannot believe Freud's statement that psycho-analysis,
purely isolated as a therapeutic method, is philosophically

neutral; that it helps to free the patient from his neurotic shackles and enables him to rediscover his basic set of beliefs, whatever they may be.

This distrust is understandable. Theoretically these statements of Freud are true. But in the reality of a living relationship between patient and physician all this is modified. The mechanism of transference and counter-transference represents many subtle currents; precisely in this lies its therapeutic strength. The unique encounter, the meeting of two human beings, with all the re-enactment of a forgotten drama, the re-presentation of that which is 'familiar' (of the family)—this is the true principle of healing. And with all this goes the unspoken, the silence, that which makes a psychic whole out of something which might be only a psychological trick. But the spirit is part of this. The philosophical setting of such a relationship does not have to be formulated to be there. The spirit of the psycho-analyst or, as it happens in many cases, his denial of the spirit comes in.

That Comtean edifice of which I spoke is already so vast that our Catholic critics come to overlook a simple fact. The psycho-analytical method in itself can be *made* philosophically neutral. There exists a number of psychiatrists, with a Christian set of beliefs, who use psycho-analytical methods with great advantage. Moreover, as we shall presently see, psycho-analysis does not quite fit in with that formidable structure philosophically and historically.

Freud in his youth was deeply influenced by Goethe's anti-mechanistic philosophy of nature. One cannot help feeling that, but for a trivial change in his own history, he might have shared the fate of other men who started off with the nineteenth-century positivist bias, and ended up by embracing metaphysical reality, as did Bergson and Whitehead. In their lives, as in Freud's, the year 1900

E

marked approximately the middle. There are more parallels. In Bergson's case the change was probably prompted by the discovery of the immediacy of psychic data. That change, that decisive transcendental move, did not come about in Freud's case. This is historically one of the reasons why psycho-analysis now forms, to a startling degree, part of the positivist revolution.

The thing to keep in mind is the fact that its roots lie somewhere else. Its basic intuitions come from a world which is quite opposed to that of scientific positivism. But there is no use fooling ourselves: this is the world by which the psycho-analytical movement has been to a large extent absorbed and assimilated. And there is no use fooling ourselves about something else. At first sight the examples given here seem disjointed and haphazard. But there is no doubt about it: the communications expert who abolishes 'value concepts' and other 'old-fashioned alternatives'; the sociologist who rejects the Christian concept of love in favour of more up-to-date psycho-analytic findings; the general who abolishes traditional morality for the establishment of a 'peace-time society'; the 'amoralist' who advocates a 'really new education for social living'; the social psychologist who investigates scientifically how to soothe the frustrations of coal miners; the zoologist who informs us about the true origins of sexual morality—they all belong together. They are signposts on the way. Ahead of us lies the fantastic possibility of a world in which human happiness is technically assembled. In that Comtean revolution there are no atrocities. There are no martyrs. Man, the image of God, is led to a painless death.

# VII   Signs of Something New

If I denounce evil as evil, is there really much gained? But if I call that bad which is actually good, great harm is done.

GOETHE, in Eckermann's *Conversations with Goethe*

The final cause is an end, and that sort of end which is not for the sake of something else, but for whose sake everything else is; so that if there is to be a last term of this sort, the process will not be infinite; but if there is no such term, there will be no final cause, but those who maintain the infinite series eliminate the Good without knowing it (yet no one would try to do anything if he were not going to come to a limit); nor would there be reason in the world.

ARISTOTLE, *Metaphysics*

FROM the preceding chapter it looks as if psycho-analysis were hopelessly interwoven with Freud's own philosophy as well as with the general nihilistic stream of our time, so much so that it would be better to leave it alone; any attempt to integrate it with a Christian philosophy of Man would be futile. Indeed this has been the feeling of many people. We have already indicated, however, how dangerous such a negative attitude can become. Having considered all the negative aspects—the 'contra'— we shall now examine the 'pro.'

To show what is in favour of the psycho-analytical theory, one can cite clinical experiences. There are various examples throughout this book which partly serve this purpose, and which indicate that the psycho-analytic interpretation illuminates the inner 'dynamics' of a case to a much greater extent than any other school of psychiatry heretofore. This refers to all kinds of troubles which arise in the psychic order, whether sexual perversions, psychoses of persecution, morbid reactions of grief, or so-called psychosomatic diseases. An apparent hodge-podge of human ills assumes something like an interior order when viewed in the light of the psycho-analytic concepts which we have outlined.

However, to what extent does psycho-analysis fit in with the Christian idea of Man?

In connection with the case history of the suicidal old immigrant, where we touched upon the concept of empathic knowledge, we examined two aspects of the process of understanding. One is empirical: we know *by experience* that under certain circumstances people look sad and cry, just as we know that under certain circumstances bubbles will begin to rise in the water inside the kettle. The other aspect to the understanding of human reactions is that we are able to be *inside* the sad individual while he tells us his story, and 'understand' his reactions in a way essentially different from the way in which we 'understand' what is going on inside the kettle. Through the development of the experimental method in the natural sciences, we have acquired to an extraordinary degree the ability to predict and 'explain' processes in inanimate nature. If one combines concentrated hydrochloric acid with a piece of marble, one is bound to obtain calcium chloride and carbon dioxide; science tells us exactly why. But it would be ridiculous to say: 'Put yourself in the marble's place. It had to react like that. You'd do the same.' *In this way* we cannot partake of the processes in inanimate nature; human consciousness is not made that way.

This distinction is very old. It goes back to Greek

philosophy and Dionysius the Areopagite.[1] Saint Thomas speaks of 'knowledge by connaturality' as opposed to other forms of knowledge in which we are not 'co-natured' with objects of the external world. Bacon's 'poesy' or poetic form of insight (as distinguished from the scientific) is related to Saint Thomas's 'knowledge by connaturality.' Bergson distinguishes 'analytical' from 'intuitive' knowledge. He illustrates this by referring to a study of movement. He takes the example of a stick drifting in a stream. He says that we can study the stick's movement in two essentially different ways. We can time the passage of the stick past certain points on the shore of the stream; from this we can describe the movement of the stick mathematically. But we also can float in the stream ourselves with the speed of the water and thus obtain an experience of movement which is essentially different from mathematical abstraction. Both approaches to movement, though independent, are equally valid. The German philosopher, Dilthey, speaks of knowledge by *Einfühlung* (there is no single word for this in English; perhaps the closest translation is 'the process of getting the feeling of something from within'). A modern school of philosophy in Germany makes a distinction similar to Bergson's, using the term 'explaining' as opposed to 'understanding.' These philosophers apply the word 'explaining' to those situations in which we deal with a chain of physical causes (the action of hydrochloric acid on marble) and the word 'understanding' to those in which we deal with a chain of motivations (the sad man's story).

Thus we can follow this distinction between two kinds of knowledge like a thread in the history of philosophical

[1] Jacques Maritain, 'On Knowledge by Connaturality,' *Review of Metaphysics*, IV, 473–478, 1951.

thought. To be sure, we have enumerated various concepts which are not identical. One cannot say that empathy, and Saint Thomas's 'knowledge by connaturality,' Bacon's idea of 'poesy,' Bergsonian 'intuitive knowledge,' the idea of '*Einfühlung*,' and the 'understanding' of recent German philosophers are different words for the same thing. But these concepts overlap to a remarkable degree, and the one feature they have in common is the assumption that there exists a method of insight which is as valid as the method of the mathematical-experimental sciences, although essentially different from it.

There is no doubt that Freud gained all his important insights by empathy. Consider, for example, the mechanism of transference. The way in which those seemingly irrational waves of affection and hostility which well up in the patient during treatment were elucidated, the way in which all the subtle currents which modify the relationship between physician and patient *were recognized for what they are*— all this is entirely removed from the world of the experimental laboratory. It is a fact that all great psycho-analytic discoveries were first of all felt from within. For a reason which we shall presently discuss, this is best seen in some of those writings which do not refer to sweeping theoretical concepts. In Freud's little-known essay on the psychology of 'the uncanny' (*das Unheimliche*), he sets out to investigate the experience of the uncanny, or the eerie. The gist of his argument is that we experience all those things as *un*canny which, in the depth of our unconscious, we actually *can* (know). As it often happens, the negation which our conscious employs (the syllable 'un') serves only to conceal that which, for some reason, we do not want to see. That which appears as eerie does so because it is the appearance of something which up to that time has led a secret life within us. Freud quotes a lot of literature to substantiate this, particularly examples from one of the poets of the weird and uncanny, the great German romantic writer, E. T. A. Hoffmann. The question whether Freud's argument is correct or not is irrelevant. The point is that this essay, in its entire structure, in the way the thought is presented and elaborated, is a perfect example of poetic knowledge. It could be an essay written by any great poet-critic from Goethe to T. S. Eliot, but it has nothing to do with natural science, with any area of human endeavour involving quantification, verification by experiment, and so on.

The fact that psycho-analytic insight is primarily empathetic insight, as contrasted with scientific knowledge, is concealed and complicated by several features, particularly by the fact that Freud himself from the beginning presented his discoveries within a framework of terms which were borrowed from the natural sciences. There are several reasons for this. The originator of psycho-analysis was a child of the nineteenth century. He had been educated in the laboratory and the neurological ward; his first studies, such as his work on infantile spastic conditions and on the pharmacology of cocaine, were purely scientific. Therefore it was most logical for him and his early followers to use the language of the natural sciences. As we have seen, there are certain aspects of physics (particularly thermodynamics) and biology (particularly ontogenesis) which lend themselves splendidly to conveying basic psycho-analytic concepts by the way of approximate analogy. When we speak of an 'amount of libidinal energy' which is 'split off' or 'channelled into' something or 'sublimated' or 'displaced,' we use the language of physicists or chemists

to make concepts out of something essentially preconceptual. The preconceptual, archaic, infantile world of
imagery, which forms the key to the world of neurosis,
reminds us of Edgar Allan Poe's 'unthought-like thoughts
that are the thoughts of thought.' Technical terminology
for such things at best partakes of the nature of parable.
As Karl Jaspers has pointed out, we fool ourselves if we
think that the terminology of psycho-analysis really proves
that it is something of the same order as physics or
chemistry. Actually, there is no such thing as an 'amount
of libidinal energy' which would fit into a system of
references comparable to that of the sciences. Love and
hate, joy and mourning cannot be quantified.

Moreover, all those forms of 'non-scientific,' intuitive
knowledge which we have been discussing, are somehow
deeply linked up with the world of values. It is noteworthy
that Saint Thomas speaks of 'knowledge by connaturality'
in connection with the moral virtues. A human being has
an immediate knowledge of concepts such as chastity,
courage, and so on because it is part of human nature to
have such knowledge. The Germans introduced the idea
of *Einfühlung* before Dilthey, in the time of Herder, in
connection with the problem of beauty. In other words,
intuitive and empathetic insight get us 'mixed up' with
values—and anyone who attempts to create something
comparable to the experimental sciences will instinctively
shy away from all this. It is historically interesting that
Jaspers' observation was anticipated a long time ago—in
fact, at the very dawn of the psycho-analytical development. When Freud's *Studies on Hysteria* appeared in 1895,
they were enthusiastically reviewed by Alfred von Berger,
professor of the history of literature at the University of
Vienna. The reviewer, who was a poet, critic, and literary

historian, remarked that 'the theory itself is in fact nothing but the kind of psychology used by poets.' He illustrated this by examples from Shakespeare.[1] In contrast, Krafft-Ebing, who was chairman of the Society of Psychiatry and Neurology in Vienna when Freud read his paper, 'The Etiology of Hysteria,' in 1896, remarked: 'It sounds like a scientific fairy tale.'[2] These were the reactions of the artist on one hand, and the nineteenth-century scientist on the other. It was only by an extraordinary feat of poetic intuition than an entire early world could possibly be opened up, a world which is still far removed from circumscribed concepts, a world of feeling—particularly of proprioceptive,[3] tactile, and gustatory (taste) feelings. It presents a sort of somatic cosmos, a huge universe of sensation, a carnal universe in which no stars or sun or moon exist, in which space and time, as far as they are there, must surely be qualities quite different from the space and time of our reasoning mind.

A most extraordinary oneness of the psychic and bodily is associated with the early Freudian ontogenetic stages. The psycho-analytical approach to psycho-somatic medicine —the field of medicine which studies the psychological roots of organic disease—helps us to see this.

For example, it has been known for some time that serious illnesses of the lower bowel (certain types of colitis) are associated with definite patterns of emotional conflict, in fact with certain character types. But it was only by psycho-analytic studies and by the introduction of psycho-analytic concepts that the relationship between those forms

[1] Ernest Jones, *The Life and Work of Sigmund Freud.* Basic Books, 1953, Vol. I, p. 253.
[2] *Ibid.*, p. 263.
[3] 'Proprioceptive' are those sensory impressions which arise from within the body, for example, the sense of impressions by which the position of joints, the tension of muscles, etc., are conveyed.

of colitis on one hand and the emotional conflict on the other were clarified. By going back to the primitive meaning of 'giving' and 'retaining' in the function of the bowel, to an early, undifferentiated, archaic psyche, such illnesses can be adequately interpreted. This interpretation is also important for their treatment.

Another example: it was first observed about thirty years ago that peptic ulcer of the stomach is associated with a certain 'nervous' type of person. It did not take long to find out that the type of person predisposed to peptic ulcer frequently has certain well-defined characteristics. They are the characteristics of a person of spartan habits, with a high sense of duty, a person who drives himself hard, a giver rather than a receiver in the exchange of life, a person of natural asceticism not infrequently found among hard-working professional people of today. One could leave it at that and say that such a person is apt to eat quickly, is unaccustomed to pay attention to the enjoyment of leisure associated with meals, and is prone to gulp down food without noticing whether it be too hot or too cold. However, careful psycho-analytic studies by Franz Alexander and his school showed that there is something more to it than that. Deep down, without being aware of it, such people have a great need to 'receive'; they are people whose hard spartan shell covers a yearning for tenderness and caressing, in other words, a yearning to be *mothered*. It is understandable, on the basis of what we have said about the embryology of love, why the stomach should be the anatomical site in which that conflict manifests itself. The psycho-analytical elucidation of such a case shows that our patient was not quite prepared to be the giver without adequately receiving. From the point of health (wholeness), there was something wrong about his spartanism.

These two examples alone imply the existence of that 'world' which corresponds largely to a preverbal stage; at any rate, to a stage in which abstract concepts are not yet formed. In that world there exists a oneness of the physical and the psychic which it is difficult to represent in our adult mode of thinking. One more example which might bring us still closer to my meaning comes from many of the expressions we use in everyday language. 'I cannot stomach him.' 'He makes me vomit.' 'I like you so much, I could eat you.' 'I took him in at a glance.' 'The milk of human kindness.' 'I'll make you eat your words.' These and many similar expressions[1] are metaphors which are coined as if eating and drinking had a significance far beyond the mere need to sustain bodily and caloric energy. Numerous psycho-analytic observations bear this out: there is an archaic phase in which the oral opening is something like an opening of the Ego through which people and objects are 'taken in,' gobbled up, destroyed or incorporated, or ejected. In this body image there is *no distinction* between the psychic and the physical, and there is no such thing as a metaphor. In this image the metaphor and the world of objective reality are one in a peculiar way which resists description for an obvious reason—our language is not made for it.

Or is it? When someone says about another person: 'I cannot stomach him,' we might be inclined to say: 'This is not to be taken literally. The stomach is a saccular enlargement of the digestive tube; it consists of a certain type of mucous membrane. This mucous membrane excretes such and such juices. Of course, the stomach is not there to take people in. It's just a silly way of wording things.'

[1] Cf. Karl Stern, J. B. Boulanger, and Sheena Cleghorn, 'The Semantics of Organ Language. A Comparative Study of English, French and German,' *American Journal of Psychiatry*, CVI, p. 851.

The psycho-analyst says: 'Such a stomach as you have just been describing is an abstraction of the anatomist. As a matter of fact, we all arise out of a world in which we *have* swallowed persons. The thing was not an anatomical mechanism; nor was it purely psychic: it was both. The description of the physiologist refers to artificially isolated phenomena. The expression, "I cannot stomach him," corresponds to a reality which we can reconstruct tediously out of the observation of the lives of children, of folk-tales, of the dreams of grown-ups, and so on. But one cannot say that that reality is a lesser reality than that of the anatomist or physiologist, the reality which is a product of abstractions.'

For hundreds of years people have been saying: 'He gets under my skin,' or 'I have been itching to do such and such.' Only now, on the basis of the psycho-analytic mode of approach, can we demonstrate objectively that skin disorders do arise out of repressed hostility or of repressed desire. For an equally long time people have been saying about one another: 'He gives me a headache,' or 'He's a pain in the neck.' Only now do we realize, on the basis of careful investigations carried out with physio-logical and psycho-analytical methods, that people do give headaches and pains to one another in quite a literal way. Before the advent of psycho-somatic medicine (which can be historically demonstrated to be a direct descendant of psycho-analysis), people would have taken the expression, 'He took it too much to heart,' as a mild poetic metaphor. Now we know that people do take 'it' to their hearts in a literal sense. The way in which we use names of organs in our language reflects the language in which these organs speak to us. All this can obviously have only one meaning: besides the anatomy of Vesalius, another kind of anatomy has always existed. One might call it folklore anatomy; one might call it poetic anatomy. The point is that in a scientific Cartesian world it is only that first kind of anatomy, the anatomy of Vesalius, that counts. The heart is a muscular pump of a certain appearance, a certain weight and a certain mechanism. The psyche, on the other hand, is a universe all by itself. In such a world it is quite impossible that 'it' can be taken to heart because 'it' and the heart belong to two universes which live side by side without communication. Yet in folklore anatomy, psycho-physical unity has always been preserved. And now this psycho-physical unity has been rediscovered under the impact of psycho-analysis. The anatomy of folklore spoke of a reality which was forgotten in a Cartesian world. This plane of reality has now been re-entered.

Thus we witness the extraordinary phenomenon that psycho-analysis, which originated in the laboratory and the clinical ward of the nineteenth century, has become a powerful current which establishes a reunion of that which man has tried to unbind or disjoint, the psychic and the physical. This current goes against all those movements from Manichæism down to Cartesianism and Positivism which have, in a sense, attempted to produce a ghastly fissure in the image of the world.

This, incidentally, is one of the reasons why in Freudian theory the 'sexual' concept is enlarged to such an extent that it comprises *eros* in the widest possible sense. Nothing puts in an appearance in a purely abstract ghost-like form. Everything psychic has its primary sensory, carnal form. A witty critic of the psycho-analytic theory once remarked that dream interpretation according to Freud is easy, since every object in nature is either convex or concave. There is some truth in this. When you consider for a moment that the masculine principle is the principle which attacks, pierces, fertilizes, and that the feminine principle is the receiving, containing, and nourishing principle, then you arrive at a continuum, a series of images which extends all the way from anatomical structures to psychic forms. If you prefer, you can invert the series. Apart from the social hierarchy of Man and Woman which fluctuates historically, there is something which one might call the Eternal-Masculine and the Eternal-Feminine in the human soul; but this is expressed in physical forms even down to the life of cells: the lance-shaped, mobile spermatozoon pierces the ovum.

Another example is that of the experience of birth. There are numerous examples to indicate that the mere act of being born is associated with anxiety. To leave the sheltering womb, to change from the passivity of placental nourishment to the act of breathing is a tremendous revolution. The first breath we breathe is associated with primeval anxiety. Being born means accepting something new and unknown and leaving security irretrievably behind. Here, too, there exists a continuum of images from the primeval carnal experience, which we all share, to thousands of other forms of being born. The idea of the Masculine and Feminine in us has been profoundly elaborated by Jung in his idea of *Animus* and *Anima*. The idea of the experience of birth has been elaborated by Otto Rank. Both are, in a sense, elaborations of Freudian concepts. What characterizes Freud's approach is the insistence on going through that continuum of images down to the soil—that is, to the carnal archaic experience in its concrete immediacy—if one wants really to understand a psychic disturbance and do anything about it. Quite irrespective of the validity of this, it is historically most remarkable and it is certainly no coincidence that in a world of mechanistic concepts and abstractions, the psychic reality could only be rediscovered by the way of the carnal.

However, what we are discussing here refers not only to the body image, but to sensory impressions and imagery in general. A middle-aged woman was having difficulties in her relationship with husband and children. The most conspicuous facts of her childhood history were these: she had been the oldest of four children, and her mother had died when she, the patient, was six years old. Shortly after that the father remarried. A lot of her childhood story was taken up by her description of a 'bad' stepmother and the disappointment over her father she experienced at the time of his second marriage. At a crucial point of her analysis, she produced the following dream: '*I saw the face of a woman. There was nothing else. Suddenly she changed into another woman. At that moment the light went off and it became dark. I called a man to put the light on again. He tried, but he did not succeed.*' She said that the appearance of the man who was unable to repair the light reminded her of the caretaker of her church. The caretaker was 'the same type' as her father.

This dream, like all dreams, is over-determined, to use psycho-analytical language. This means it can be interpreted on different levels of the patient's history, and various interpretations are correct. There is the history of the two mother figures, and of the father who, in her fantasy, failed to put on the light after it had gone out. The situation of transference is also implied. The doctor was clearly at fault in his inability to find the light. If the patient lacked insight, it was I who did not throw light on the situation. From a technical point of view there are many facets to this dream which are not related to the present phase of our discussion. I should like to discuss only one.

Here light stands for love, and darkness for the opposite, lack of love. With the appearance of the second woman the light goes out. The dream uses the same imagery as the poets and mystics of all ages. One might explain this quite simply. To be left alone in the dark is the earliest experience associated with a farewell from mother or from others close to us. Or there might be something less relative, something more intimately related to the experience of light and darkness. The important thing is the fact that in the language of the dream we encounter light, a basic sensory experience, just as basic as the feelings arising from within the body or from the skin, and we find that it *is* at the same time, in some peculiar way, love.

We moderns are biased in such a way that we think that the 'true nature' of light is represented only by Newton's corpuscular theory, or Huygens's wave theory, or the quantum theory (which is a sort of synthesis of the two). We forget that these are mathematical abstractions, and that the simple act of seeing is the only way for us to experience light. Newton created our currently accepted theory of colours. Goethe, who was in a continuous revolt against the rationalism of the eighteenth century, evolved another theory of colours which is non-mathematical and 'naïve'; it is more of a physiology of colours. No physicist takes Goethe's theory seriously. Goethe fought an almost Quixotic battle against the theory of Newton. He never came to admit that reality can be presented on different planes, and in each single instance the presentation is true.

Newtonian light, the light of primary sensory experience,

and the 'metaphoric' light of Platonists and poets and of Saint John ('in Him was life, and the life was the light of men and the light shineth in the darkness, and the darkness did not comprehend it'), are three different aspects of the same thing. Now the first aspect does not exist in the world of the unconscious. There we encounter only the light of immediate sensory experience, and the setting in which we encounter it is such that it is intimately associated with the third aspect, the spiritual light, the light of the poetic metaphor. Here the reality of logical abstraction does not play any role; on the other hand, the two other levels (sensory imagery and its metaphoric 'sphere') penetrate one another to a degree which is known to us only from poetry.

Our modern mind is such that deep down we harbour some sort of hierarchy of realities: we more or less feel that the reality of physics is the objective thing, that the reality of our sense perceptions is less reliable, and the reality of allegory is most arbitrary and unreliable. This was not always so. When Saint Thomas, for example, in his commentary on the Gospel of Saint John speaks of 'Light,' he changes from the sensory to the spiritual and back again, as if he regarded both planes as of equal validity. We must leave it to the philosophers to explain whether there is a spiritual reality which corresponds to the reality of sensory perception, and which is not just an outcome of a haphazard play of verbal parallels. For anyone acquainted with the Platonist-Augustinian tradition, which enters strongly into the thought of Saint Thomas, such a picture of the world comes as close to an adequate presentation of reality as anything ever will. It is interesting to note that a philosopher of nature like Goethe, who had no formal knowledge of Christian philosophy, went very far in this direction. At the end of *Faust*, during a poetic description of the Beatific Vision, occur the following famous lines:

> *All that which passes*
> *Is mere Analogy,*
> *The Unattainable*
> *Here is Reality*

From such examples as our patient's dream and even more so the symbols of 'organ language' in their relation to psycho-somatic medicine, it looks almost as if psycho-analysis had come to rediscover something like the reality of the allegorical.

We have seen aspects of psycho-analysis which lift it out of the currents of our century, the century of dialectic materialism and of logical positivism, right into the mainstream of the Hebrew-Christian and Hellenic tradition: the eminent role of the function of empathy (which is related to knowledge by connaturality); the trend to re-establish a psycho-physical unity in the concept of the human person; moreover the 'reality of the allegorical.' These features alone should make psycho-analysis as a discipline suspect in the eyes of all materialistic thinkers.

However, there is another feature which moves the Freudian concept of the personality even closer to a quasi-metaphysical position: the ontogenetic theory. What does the Freudian schema of 'stages' actually mean? What is implied by the entire sequence from an early undifferentiated quantum of libidinal energy which rests in itself, and at the same time extends in an ill-defined way into the world of objects, from that through the oral and anal phase to the first genital phase, through the phase of latency to the phase

of puberty, from puberty to a stage of love which continuously sacrifices parts of itself? It is a tremendous story
of unfolding. However, any process of unfolding becomes
meaningful only by that which is to be unfolded. If anything develops it is the end towards which it develops
which gives meaning to the development. To a botanist
who studies all the phases of an oak, from the acorn to
the mature tree, his observations make sense only because
he has the end, namely the oak, in view. I remember how
fascinated we used to be by our lectures in embryology. We
happened to have a professor who was an extraordinarily
gifted teacher. But the thrill which he was able to convey
was due to the fact that we knew the outcome of the whole
thing—the human form. The cluster of cells called morula
possessed a meaning by virtue of the idea of a developed
human being. The idea of a process of becoming without
the idea of finality is a paradox. The fact that something
unfolds possesses a meaning only by virtue of that into
which it finally develops, is called entelechy.

It is the tragedy of psycho-analysis that it was evolved
by a nineteenth-century scientist who was very careful to
remain what one used to call 'scientific.' In order to remain
scientific, in that sense, you have to exclude anything which
is transcendental, in other words, which 'goes beyond' that
which is perceived by our senses and can be measured.
Entelechy is a transcendental principle. If one stops to
think what makes an acorn develop into an oak tree, one
has already gone beyond science. One can describe and
measure the plant in each phase of that development. One
can divide this movement up into one hundred thousand
or one million 'stills,' but the movement itself, the process
of becoming, is more than a sequence of one million simple
phases—it is a flow in which the end (tree) is already

contained in the beginning (acorn). Or, differently expressed, the acorn contains a potential principle which points beyond itself towards the tree.

One may assume that most embryologists of the nineteenth century had the characteristic positivist outlook of the scientists of their time; in that case, they had, strictly speaking, chosen the wrong field. If when asked, 'Why are you studying all these various phases in the life of the embryo?' the student answers, 'Because I am interested in the way the finished human form comes into being,' he has confessed to a metaphysical outlook, whether he knows it or not. He implies a *design*. However, in the case of an embryologist of the body this is not so obvious, and one can perhaps disguise it. Not so in the case of an embryologist of the psyche. The moment we introduce the Freudian ontogenetic principle into psychology, we leave the world of experimental psychology with its stop-watches, tape measures and graphs behind, and enter the world of an *unfolding form*. It is easy for an embryologist to find a title for his story. He might call it, 'From the primitive cell to the human body.' For a man who writes on the development of the person it is much more difficult to find an appropriate title: 'From primitive narcissism to . . .' To what? 'From primitive narcissism to maturity.' But 'maturity' is only another word for the end of a process of development. It can have only two meanings, the first of which is relative and therefore temporal. A Chinese, a Russian, or an Englishman, or representatives of three different centuries of the same country, would probably have entirely different definitions of what they call mature. Even so, the definitions would still be arbitrary; in the case of Russia it would depend a lot on whether Lenin or Tolstoy did the defining. If we accept a genetic theory of the person,

149     SIGNS OF SOMETHING NEW

then the primeval psychic structure must contain potentially the psychic form very much as the simple cell contains the physical form—the end must give a *meaning* to the beginning in a manner which transcends all social or economic or historical determinants. This is the second meaning of maturity: there must be a design for Man.

In the seventh book of the *Republic*, Plato tells the famous parable of the cave. It is the story of prisoners in an underground den, chained in such a way that they are unable to move their heads around towards the den's opening. Outside the den, in the light, figures of men are walking. Some of these men are carrying objects. Beyond those figures a fire is blazing so that the shadows of the moving figures are thrown against the cave's wall. And beyond the fire is the sun in the sky. These moving shadows then are the only things the prisoners are able to see. They can have no concept of the origins of the shadows. As is well known, in this parable the figures and objects outside the cave represent *ultimate reality*, the world of Ideas, and we are the prisoners who, in this life, are able to see only dim shadows. Plato tells us how the released prisoner is in such a state that in the beginning he finds it difficult to discern the real persons and the objects they are carrying. 'When he approaches the light his eyes will be dazzled, and he will not be able to see anything at all of what we now call realities.' When the prisoner returns to the den, he is first at a disadvantage compared with his fellow prisoners. 'Imagine once more, I said, such a one coming suddenly out of the sun to be replaced in his old situation; would he not be certain to have his eyes full of darkness? . . . Men would say of him that up he went and down he came without his eyes; and that it was better not even to think of ascending.'[1] If we disregard for the moment the relationship between ultimate reality and mere shadow which exists in Plato's philosophy, this parable serves well to illustrate the point to which we have come.

The resistance against the sexual theory of Freud is not only due to the fact that the theory is 'sexual.' Many people who are free from prudishness share that resistance. Anyone who comes out from a world which is bathed in the light of reason into the embryonic night of the flesh; from the clear landscape of everyday wakeful thinking into a world of archaic somatic imagery; from a world in which Vergil's poems and Bach fugues symbolize an ultimate meaningfulness into a world of 'castration fear' and 'oral destructiveness'; anyone who enters that pre-rational world from the light outside is like one of Plato's returning prisoners. He cannot see anything.

The reverse, however, is also true. If someone comes to believe that the Freudian concepts are all there is to the nature of Man, he loses sight of the ultimate design. The seemingly bizarre and fantastic Freudian story of a libidinal chrysalis makes sense only if there is an image of the human personality which is beyond that and yet completely real. Freud has beautifully described the healthy development of the person, from narcissism to object-relationship—that is to say, from an undifferentiated, pre-ideational, amorphous conglomerate of feeling towards a person with a capacity to love. The Christian goes one step further. He gives transcendental coherence to the story. Love is God. God gives an ultimate meaning to human existence. To come back to Plato's parable, beyond the cave, beyond the figures, beyond the fire, is the Eternal Sun.

It will be recalled that in Plato's parable the returning

[1] *The Republic*, translation by B. Jowett.

prisoners, who tell about the things they have encountered
in the light outside the cave, are received with hostility by
their fellows. Indeed, there seems to be an element of
hostility and destructiveness in all materialist and reductive
philosophers. There is an element of spite in debunking.
Max Scheler and, even more so, Gabriel Marcel have
emphasized how full of resentment the Marxists are when
they indulge in their philosophy of 'nothing but.' This view
is not completely justified. Both Marx and Freud were
sensitive to the lies and the hypocrisy of the society in
which they lived. The 'nothing but,' with all its crude
materialism, implies apart from the *ressentiment* a moral
movement, a holy impatience, something of the prophetic
spirit of the Old Testament. If Marx, instead of saying,
'Religion is nothing but the opiate of the people,' had told
some of the members of the ruling class of the early
industrialist period, 'Woe unto you who use religion as
an opiate for the people,' he would have had a strong
point. Many people, from the Prophet Isaiah to Léon Bloy,
have said the same thing. If Freud had told some of his
patients, 'What you call religion is actually your neurosis,'
instead of claiming that religion *is* a neurosis, he would
have stated a frequently observed truth. If they are taken
in the proper spirit, the debunkers fulfil an important
function. They stir us out of our complacency. We see so
frequently in practice that 'religion' is unconsciously used
as a channel of aggressiveness. The Reverend Mr Davidson,
in Somerset Maugham's *Rain*, is a famous example of
something which, unfortunately, is commonplace. It is also
possible that a young woman who joins a religious community which occupies itself particularly with unmarried
mothers may be in an inner state which makes her unable
to provide motherly or sisterly love to such girls; she may

enter on this path not in a spirit of charity but, unknowingly, out of unresolved conflicts which make for cruelty. Of course, common sense has always known about this. Such things have recently provided themes, perhaps influenced by psycho-analysis, for Catholic novelists. What should be emphasized here is the fact that the 'nothing but,' though philosophically wrong, contains a movement towards moral purification.

This point is closely related to something else. Anyone who has been able to gain psycho-analytic insight must feel humbled. A gaze into the interior reveals a great deal of frailty of which we have never been aware. A parade of human misery files past in our clinics, suicide and murder, cynicism and despair, drunkenness and promiscuity, miserliness and suspicion—and all the time you feel: 'But for a trivial difference of circumstances, not at all merited, there go I.' The moral values have not changed. But it has become quite difficult for one to feel superior. As a matter of fact, according to psycho-analytical teaching you have to know your own depth first to be able to help these people precisely because they represent your own latent possibilities. This is a challenge to Christian consciousness.

It is also the reason why, if somebody's moral philosophy is based on the Judaeo-Christian tradition, the acquaintance with psycho-analysis often deepens his natural charity. The judge of a juvenile court, a man of deep religious convictions, once told me how his attitude towards the delinquent had changed ever since he had taken instruction in the psychology of his young defendants. This instruction had been given to him by a professor of psychology, a Dominican priest who was psycho-analytically orientated. The judge told me that he used to be rigid and dry, relying on the letter of the law, in his attitude towards the youngsters. In retrospect it seemed to him that he had got nowhere. This man, who goes into meditation before each court session, told me that now he *understood* and tried to love these young people. When he talked to them, it was as if he felt what they must be feeling. He said that the result of his work was so much enhanced that it now seemed as different as day from night. A Catholic psycho-analyst from France once remarked that his charity was enormously deepened ever since he himself had been analysed. This has nothing to do with moral relativism; it means only that the hard soil of receptivity has been ploughed and enriched.

From what we have said in this chapter two things have become clear. First, psycho-analysis contains precious elements which point in the direction of a Christian personalism. In order to see this one has to divest it of the philosophy of its founder, and of all the accretions which have been gathering to embed it in the current of 'the third revolution.' Second, while no psychological discovery, however startling, can undo or reshape Christian values, on the plane of practical exigencies—in the educational field, in the field of therapy, and so on—those who regard the Gospel as the basis for their lives can only gain from all genuine discoveries. For the rest of this book, we shall enlarge on these two points.

# VIII
Guilt and Anxiety

The problem of evil and of wrongdoing is part and parcel of the problem of freedom.

N. BERDYAEV, *Dostoievsky*

ONE aspect of present-day psychiatry, and of psychoanalysis in particular, which evokes in many people a sense of apprehension and distrust, is the problem of guilt. It would almost seem as if the reality of good and evil, of innocence and culpability, were being questioned with the advent of 'depth psychology.'

There have, of course, always been extreme cases in which everybody acknowledged that a morally reprehensible act had been carried out under conditions which exclude guilt. If someone commits murder while insane, the judgment of common sense and of the law courts regards him as a patient rather than a criminal. The so-called McNaghten rule in British law reflects this attitude, though the courts do not always accept expert psychiatric testimony with regard to insanity. If the railway worker described in Chapter III committed acts of delinquency after the crowbar accident which deprived him of his frontal lobes, it was obvious to his pre-Freudian contemporaries that he was not guilty in any moral sense. However, even in such cases of organic impairment of the function of the brain, the question of guilt was not always unequivocal. In certain types of organic illness of the brain, an attack may occur during which the patient is not conscious of what he is doing, although all his actions seem well co-ordinated. Occasionally in such a state a crime is committed. Some psychiatrists of previous generations hesitated to regard such an organic condition as an exculpating element in the case of a crime, because it was impossible to prove that the patient's consciousness was altered while the crime was committed. There is no doubt that under this theory many a man has been innocently condemned.

The situation is complicated by the fact that many patients with organic disorders of the brain have also psychogenic (psychologically determined) disturbances. Automatic actions which appear well co-ordinated, but which occur in a state of altered consciousness, have been known for a long time. The French clinicians used to call them 'fugues' and in German medical literature they are referred to as 'twilight states.' When they appear in the daily newspaper, they are described as 'amnesia.' A patient 'comes to' in a place which is strange to him, and claims not to know how he got there. Investigation reveals that he must have carried out complicated actions for several hours or even days while in a clouded state; yet he has no recollection of the entire period. Such an occurrence may be purely psychogenic. William James's famous Mr Brown, who one day found himself in a store selling groceries and who a few months before had been a minister in another town, is undoubtedly a 'twilight' case. Ogden Nash's absent-minded Professor Primrose may belong in the same class. In classical psychiatric literature, until one was able to record the electro-potentials of the brain, there used to be a simple rule of thumb for all such cases: when in doubt, find out whether there is a motive for escape in the life situation of the patient. If there is, then his 'twilight' attack was psychologically determined. If not, there was likely to be an organic disorder of the brain. (William James's and Ogden Nash's patients, although the authors make no point of it, must have had 'motives for escape.') Long-lasting twilight states are possibly always of psychogenic origin.

Today, when we know something about the electro-potentials of the human brain, things are no longer so simple. During the war, a boy of fourteen whose aunt told me that he had the habit of suddenly disappearing, was treated. After his disappearance he would turn up the following morning in some such place as a downtown back-yard, without the slightest notion how he got there and what had happened during the intervening time. When I spoke to the boy, he told me that his father was overseas and that he and his mother, who worked, were boarding with an uncle and aunt. The boy described the uncle as 'very hard' and 'down on me.' The old rule of thumb pro-vided a 'motive for escape,' but just to be on the safe side the aunt was asked about a possible history of brain injury. She remembered that at the age of nine the boy had been hit by a streetcar, and his skull fractured. Tracing the electro-potentials revealed a pattern typical of so-called 'psychic seizures' in the area of one of the temporal lobes of the brain. Before the discovery of electro-encephalography, the boy's 'twilight' state would certainly have been regarded as of a purely 'psychological' nature. This story is told first to show that a state of disturbance may be organically caused and yet its *content*—the actual choice[1] of symptoms —may be psychologically determined. Secondly, in the minds of most people, an organically caused disturbance

[1] The word 'choice' here does not imply a conscious, intentional act.

cannot possibly be associated with the concept of guilt, while a psychologically motivated disturbance is not so easily exculpated. The dichotomy is no longer as simple as one used to think.

If our young patient had hit his uncle over the head, and claimed loss of memory during this act, the situation would have been quite complex. Before the era of electroencephalography, a great number of experts would have regarded him as guilty. It is not at all clear why this should be so. The fact remains that to many people the world of physical cause and effect is associated with determinism, the world of motives (psychological causes) with freedom.

Then there is the question of the subjective experience of guilt. Many psychiatric patients have ideas of guilt which are obviously morbid. Most lay people are able to spot delusions of guilt; in fact, there is something quite startling about them. An admired and respectable citizen, known for a life of integrity, suddenly commits suicide. Such a catastrophe is frequently due to the sudden eruption of irrational self-accusations. There is a state around the middle or the early decline of life which is characterized by such a seemingly mysterious eruption. The victims are usually people who have been over-conscientious rather than the opposite throughout their lives. We know now that their over-conscientiousness represents in latent, potential form the fiery lava of guilt which finally descends on them; this has been borne out by psycho-analytical studies. Some patients see their entire past as drenched in 'sin,' while others pick out some trivial incident and magnify it to bizarre dimensions.

An elderly lady, a dutiful housewife and mother, who had nursed her husband faithfully for two years during a final illness, broke down after his death. She was brought to the hospital in an agitated state of despair. Nothing, not even capital punishment, she said, would be enough to atone for what she had done. Finally, with signs of dread, she revealed that thirty years before she had done something very wrong. During subsequent interviews it became evident that a friend of her husband's had on one occasion made a harmless 'pass' at her while she was alone with him. It is important to know that her husband had been a drinker, difficult to get along with, and particularly aggravating during his final illness. According to her daughter, who supplied this part of the information, the mother had borne her husband's behaviour with great patience until she finally succumbed to this morbid depression, albeit only after his death. We shall not go into the psycho-analytical interpretation of this story. It is quoted only to illustrate with a particularly crude example the discrepancy between objective guilt, on the one hand, and the subjective experience of guilt on the other. In this case there is no guilt at all. However, there are degrees in the experience of real guilt and these degrees are just as puzzling to the observer as the affliction of the melancholy widow. Tolstoy describes vividly the tortures of remorse to which Anna Karenina finally succumbs; at the same time other ladies of high Russian society talk casually about their extramarital exploits in the manner in which one discusses sports events, without the least sign of bad conscience. There lies a mystery.

The problem of guilt is inextricably interwoven with the problem of anxiety.

A student nurse was so tense and anxious that she found herself unable to go on with her studies. Whenever she was called to the office of the head nurse, the superintendent of nursing, or in fact any woman who was above her in the hierarchy of nursing, she developed a rapid pulse, her knees began to shake, her voice became hoarse, she grew pale and her eyes had a fearful expression. This reaction did not develop because of an expected reproach; it accompanied any routine call. Nor did it depend on whether there was anything severe or forbidding in her superior's manner. The girl was intelligent and pleasant, and her record at the nursing school was good. Yet she felt that her reaction was uncontrollable and that it was sufficient reason for her to stop her career. It did not take long to find out that any female person in authority unconsciously represented a maternal image to the patient. Any maternal image inspired fear. But the true origin of fear was the girl's own hostile reaction to the mother, a reaction of which she had never become conscious and which she had never solved.

In following the case only to this point, we see three things: the reaction of fear in the absence of objective danger; the fact that the feared object represents something else in disguise—namely, some archaic image which must be endowed with extraordinary power; and a poorly controlled force within the anxious subject.

What does this mean? The word fear is used by psychologists to connote the reaction of the organism to danger. If one walks alone in the forest and is confronted by a wild animal, one experiences the emotional state called 'fear,' and at the same time one has all the physical symptoms which our student nurse reported. The skin is pale, the mouth feels dry, the heart beats fast, the knees shake, the pupils dilate, one may have a tendency to empty bowels and bladder. If the blood could be examined biochemically at that moment, one would discover certain things in addition, such as the fact that the blood sugar is rising. The great American physiologist, Cannon, has developed a widely known hypothesis concerning this reaction. He drew people's attention to the fact that all these autonomic[1] reactions are controlled by the medulla of the adrenal gland and the sympathetic nervous system. Then he stated hypothetically that the entire reaction had a teleological significance or, in other words, a meaningful purpose. The 'meaning' of this reaction, according to Cannon, is to prepare the organism either for fight or flight. The skin turns pale, because all the blood supply is geared to be at the disposal of the muscles; the muscles become tense to the degree of tremor to be ready for action; the blood sugar rises in order to supply the muscles with food; the pupils dilate to enable one to see as well as possible; the bowels and bladder are emptied to make the body light. Incidentally there are neuro-physiological data which would indicate that animals may have all these reactions without the subjective emotional state which we call 'fear.'

Neurotic anxiety is defined as fear without danger. If one adopts Cannon's teleological theory of fear, one faces a remarkable paradox—there is good reason to believe that even in the presence of objective danger many situations occur in which the physiological reactions associated with fear are no longer meaningful for man. If you were to find yourself alone in your house at night, knowing that a man with a gun had sneaked in to kill you, it is doubtful that your organism would be more easily defended if you quickly emptied your bowels and bladder before meeting him. In other words, there are many situations, at least for civilized man, in which the physiological reaction of fear is

[1] 'Autonomic' because most of these reactions cannot be controlled by our intention. You can wilfully open or close your fist, but you cannot wilfully make your pupils wider or narrower, your heart beat faster, etc.

meaningless, from the point of view of Cannon's criteria, or even harmful.

In the case of anxiety the situation is even more paradoxical, because no objective danger appears to be present. Our student nurse behaves *as if* there were a tiger in the underbrush, or *as if* there were a gunman waiting in the dark. It is one of the merits of Freud to have shown that a danger actually does exist in these situations. However, contrary to the reaction of normal fear in man, the source of danger lies not in the outside world but within the depth of the person. The situation of the student nurse is somewhat similar to those picture puzzles we used to study when we were children. A pen-and-ink drawing of many intricate lines would be presented with a caption: 'Where is the tiger?' or 'Where is the dog?' or 'Where is the child?' Only after studying the drawing from many angles did the missing figure become discernible. Our student nurse who experiences all of Cannon's symptoms poses the question: 'Where is the tiger?'

Psycho-analytic theory claims *the tiger must be somewhere*. Since we cannot see him, we must look for him, in contrast to the situation described in the famous poem, inside the lady. Consider this extraordinary phenomenon. Not only is there an aspect to the reaction of fear which makes it appear anachronistic, even under the circumstances of objective danger—as if the human organism had to repeat reactions which at one time were meaningful —but there is the further element that our young lady reacts to an image of her inner reality, an image which looms in the subterranean layers of her person ready to endow the harmless figures of objective reality with immensely threatening power.

The mystery of anxiety and guilt comes more clearly

F

into view when we approach certain cases of phobia—that is, anxiety which is not 'diffuse' but tends to be associated with certain situations. A young married woman was obsessed with a panic-like fear of eating in the presence of strangers. She could not accept dinner invitations, she could not eat in restaurants, or in any situation which involved anyone except her husband. There was one abnormal feature about her childhood on which she dwelt at length: she referred to it as a 'foreigner complex.' She was born in Canada of parents who had immigrated from Yugoslavia. Her mother tongue was English and, as far as appearance and language were concerned, there was nothing to distinguish her from other North American girls. Yet her Slav name bothered her a lot. At school she felt that she had been regarded as 'the Polack'; particularly during extra-curricular activities, such as recreation or choir practice, she felt decidedly the 'outsider,' the Yugoslav girl who was not considered as belonging to the group. There were eight children in her family, five girls and three boys. First came a boy followed by three girls, then came twins (a boy and a girl), then another boy and the last child was a girl. Our patient was the girl twin.

There were many indications that she had appeared at an awkward moment in the history of her family. After the three girls one child, the boy, would have been enough —to put it in a way in which it was probably never consciously formulated by anyone in the family. As is well known, parents' feelings at the arrival of children are not always feelings of love and acceptance. There is a great body of scientific evidence to prove the Freudian contention (originally an hypothesis) that the mother's anxiety and her ambivalent feelings during the early phase of feeding have a decisive influence on the world of feelings in which the child finds himself when grown up. According to that Freudian 'embryology,' the earliest fantasies of destruction are those associated with biting and swallowing. In our patient's setting all the food of love had to go for two, and it is not difficult to see the point in psycho-analytical theory. Eating together is the oldest symbol of fraternal love; Plato's *Symposium* is the love-feast *par excellence*. Yet it was just the idea of the shared meal which struck terror into our patient's heart, so that she began to tremble at the approach of the situation. This interpretation was borne out by the material she provided under treatment. That world of troglodytes, with its law of 'devour or be devoured,' is potentially slumbering in all of us. Her particular history had been such that this law still entered into her relationship with other people. Incidentally, the story of her 'foreigner complex' also becomes more understandable: the fact that in early child-hood she had the feeling of being the undesired one, the intruder in the group, had been repressed. It was trans-posed, as it were, on to the social and racial plane, a plane on which it was also more easily tolerated than in its original form. What little we have discussed about this patient's case is enough to indicate a few important points. 'Fear without objective danger' becomes meaningful if we trace it back to its original setting. The 'unfinished business' of early history is re-enacted in situations which bear all the characteristics of disguise; the original tragedy becomes all but unrecognizable.

Two more examples will illustrate what we want to say about the problem of objective guilt as compared to neurotic guilt. A prominent business man from out-of-town was first seen in a hotel in Montreal. He was in bed in a suite on the first floor, under the influence of alcohol and barbiturates,

but still in a depressed and anxious mood. His state was
so deplorable that I felt he might have to go to hospital.
When I mentioned this he became, like so many patients,
even more anxious, but the reason he gave was curious: he
was afraid he might have to be put on one of the 'higher'
floors of the hospital. By this he meant any floor above
the third. For several years he had been suffering from a
morbid fear of heights, so much so that he could not attend
any business meetings in the usual tall office buildings
without 'doping himself' with great amounts of sedatives.
Even then he often had to leave the meeting in an inner
state of panic after ten minutes, using any excuse which
came to mind. During the war he had some important
government function besides his business and at times he
would be summoned on short notice to go somewhere by
plane. It was often necessary for him to refuse. While his
history was being taken he suddenly said: 'I am going to
tell you something you ought perhaps to know. I've never
told this to anybody before. . . .' He had grown up in the
north of England under very poor circumstances. His father
had been a pedlar. 'I used to get along well with my father,
I think, but one day we had a most awful row, and I told
him I wished he were dead. And the most extraordinary
thing happened. That very day my father went out and
never returned. He was drowned in the moors.'

Without going into the remaining details of this man's
history, something should be mentioned at this point. We
not infrequently see men who suffer from what one might
call 'fear of success.' Just when they are at the height of
their career, they do something to fail; they engineer this
failure with the sureness of a sleep-walker and one can often
show conclusively that the failure has been engineered as a
kind of atonement. In these cases success, in the language of

their unconscious, means a tremendous aggression against the father, and failure is an irrational penance which is attained with an inner necessity which is startling. This necessity is reminiscent of the compelling force of the laws which govern the physical universe. Though no such failure had yet occurred in our patient at this time, it soon became apparent that his fear of heights was to be understood metaphorically. He had had a rocket-like career, which put him 'high above' the father's position in life. But when he had reached the zenith, he became panic-stricken by height in the literal, spatial sense.

As a matter of fact, it is perhaps incorrect to say that his fear of heights is to be understood metaphorically. On the contrary it is almost as if our everyday metaphors are to be understood in terms of such things as our patient's phobia. In the world of our unconscious, there is no such thing as 'high above' in a purely figurative sense. In that area of existence everything is matter, and there is nothing outside matter. It is one thing to say figuratively 'I have soared so high, I'm dizzy with success.' But it is truly horrible to endure this concretely, in a world in which, as we have shown, metaphor and reality are one.

It is a well-known fact that the first dream which the patient recounts during his first session is frequently a 'give-away.' It is almost as if, in anticipation of that first interview, the unconscious makes a frantic attempt at a solution of conflicts. A young man was interviewed in a serious anxiety state with depression; he literally trembled and cried. He was of eastern European descent, and one of the main features of the family situation was a rigid and autocratic father. Almost all the other members of his family had been seen for various neurotic conditions. The patient's

depression, with all the details of its development, was most
characteristic of situations of repressed aggressiveness with
guilt and self-punishment. During the first session he was
asked whether he might be able to recite any dream he
happened to remember. He said that only the night before
he had dreamed the following: '*I found myself in a room I
did not recognize. I had in my hand a long pointing stick, one
of those things lecturers use for pointing at lantern slides. I
pointed at a light above me. I touched it with the stick and
it broke. That moment I heard my father's voice behind me
saying: "You'll pay for this!" I turned around, saw my father
standing right behind me, and woke up.*' This 'first' dream
was crucial in a typical way; it contained in a condensed
version the mechanism of his anxiety state. Knowing his
family and knowing something about the inner meaning
of his illness, it had already been suspected that his father
had made him pay for something. The dream confirmed
this suspicion. Even without the orthodox methods of
dream analysis, one can say that he must at one time have
felt threatened by reprisals for his phallic aggressiveness
(the pointing rod). 'The light above' may stand for authority,
or the lamp may have a maternal and feminine significance
—this would depend on other psychological material, and
it is of no particular interest to us at this moment.

These three examples all have certain features in common. As I have already indicated above, they all refer to
a world of archaic imagery. This world, which is fantastic
compared to the world of objective reality in which the
adult moves, is at the same time purely concrete; it consists
only of somatic and spatial concreteness. One could say
that 'guilt' is actually an abstract concept, and in such a
world of early fantasy the abstract concept has no place.

Secondly, the fantasy of aggression and destruction on

one hand and the fantasy of punishment on the other are so intricately interlaced that it is hard to say what is actually the source of anxiety. After working with these patients, one is almost tempted to say that it is purely academic to know which it is that inspires anxiety—grinding the brother up or being ground up, outdoing the father or being outdone. The fact that in the beginning there is no abstract concept, but merely a spatial and somatic image, with certain physiological equivalents—is again apparent in the etymology of many words. For example, *remorse* is, literally speaking, 'that which *bites back*.' The reversal of oral aggression, as the earliest and crudest prototype of that which we later call guilt, is clearly expressed in this. Remorse, in that naked somatic sense, is never experienced by a healthy person. Only our lady who was terrified of eating in the presence of other people experienced *remorse* on that level of primeval concreteness.

Thirdly, if we interpret the three instances as instances of self-punishment, we see another remarkable feature: in objective reality there is either nothing, or very little, to punish. The patient is afraid of a danger which does not really exist, and this danger represents a punishment for something he desired to do but never did. The widow who broke down with morbid delusions of guilt after her husband's death felt guilty about a harmless incident with one of her husband's friends thirty years before. Psycho-analysis would demonstrate (in cases in which analytical investigation is possible) that at that time she most probably had strong temptations which were repressed. Under certain psychological constellations, repressed wishes evoke more violent guilt feelings than many real acts which, from the point of view of Christian morality, are objectively wrong. In the case of our widow, we also see that that force which produces the experience of guilt in her, has a quality which one might call *maximalism* if this word were not already used for something else. In the fantasy of these patients, nothing short of complete and utter annihilation will do for atonement, and no forgiveness is possible. This becomes quite clear in psychotic depressions. But even in the two cases of phobia (fear of eating and of height), the anxiety has this 'all-out' quality. True guilt is related to debt. In several languages, the words for guilt and debt are synonymous. But the 'guilt' which we have encountered in our three cases has, unlike true debt, an element of inexhaustibility. It cannot be paid off and be done with.

In this connection it is necessary to refer once more to compulsive-obsessive states. Everybody experiences compulsive-obsessive symptoms, if not in their fullness at least as little quirks. We have already said that almost everyone, particularly during adolescence, goes through a phase during which he 'has to do funny things,' such as avoiding the cracks in the pavement, or counting windows, or skipping every second step on the staircase, or going back a certain number of times to see whether the gas tap is closed or the door is locked at night. The German novelist Jean Paul describes a schoolmaster who had to crawl out of bed several times at night to see in the light of the moon whether his shoes were placed perfectly parallel. The composer Anton Bruckner was tortured by a compulsion to count windows, and frequently he had to return to his study to make sure that the manuscript of a symphony was covered by an extra sheet of paper.

In some people, these compulsions become so serious that they can badly handicap the patient's life. They certainly deprive him of his happiness. What the Catholic theologian calls 'scruples' also belong in this category. In retrospect the person finds a flaw in his confession, and has to make it over and over again. Or he has to repeat a certain prayer over and over, because something may have been wrong with it. One peculiar aspect of compulsions is that the patient has partial or full insight: he knows that the act he feels compelled to carry out is 'crazy,' and yet the compelling force seems irresistible. Moreover, when he makes an effort to resist the compulsion (for example, if he tries hard *not* to count the windows), he is filled with anxiety which gradually mounts until he carries his ritual out; then a momentary relief from tension follows until the first faint impulse appears again.

Closely related to those compulsive states are cases of a 'compulsive character,' as they are commonly called. These people, unlike compulsive-obsessive neurotics, do not suffer subjectively and would never seek the help of a psychiatrist. Everybody knows someone of a compulsive character in his own personal experience. The office manager cannot begin his work in the morning unless three sharpened pencils lie in parallel arrangement on the right side of the blotter, the calendar is at the left top side of the blotter, the files are clipped together in sequence, and there is a perfectly clean sheet of blotting-paper. If any of these things is not 'just so,' the manager is disturbed; he is either unable to work, or he starts off the day on the wrong foot. It is often difficult for this type of person to regard his work as finished because there are always a few minor items invisible to the naked eye to adjust before the work can be thought complete. In everyday psychology a person of such a compulsive character is therefore referred to as a 'perfectionist.' Though such a person does not necessarily suffer himself, he may cause suffering in those around him.

Closely related to compulsive acts as encountered in compulsive neurosis are obsessive thoughts. These are thoughts which 'come to' the patient apparently against his will, and are recognized, with full insight, as morbid. The patient 'has to' think an obscene word during a certain prayer or during a ceremonial reception, or the sight of any sharp instrument suggests the idea of killing his own children. It can easily be seen how alarming this symptom may be to the patient.

When we contemplate the subjective aspect (phenomenology) of these symptoms, they all have something in common. The patient seems to say: 'I know this is crazy, but *I cannot resist it.*' Carried to its logical conclusion, this means that an idea is an extraneous something which enters the mind, and not something produced actively. This is not as paradoxical as it sounds. Even under normal circumstances there are two elements to the subjective experience of thinking. When one says, 'I could not rest until I had this mathematical problem solved,' one thinks of one's consciousness as an agent. When one says, 'I was sitting on a bench when the thought occurred . . .' one thinks of one's consciousness as a recipient. The great French psychiatrist Pierre Janet, the most important forerunner of Freud, called people with compulsive-obsessive symptoms *psychasthenic*. This expression implied that their psyche was too weak to prevent certain thoughts from intruding. It even implied that the healthy psyche is strong enough to keep those thoughts 'out,' but that they are potentially there to pounce on it. This concept of Janet's conjures up an image of consciousness comparable to a torch-lit camp in the jungle surrounded by animals prowling in the dark, and ready to intrude the moment the fire goes out and the defences are weakened.

When we contemplate the *content* of these symptoms, we make a simple observation. These examples of compulsive acts all resemble penances. An over-strict parent or a cruel headmaster could say: 'You go back and do these stairs over again, and woe unto you if there is even a suspicion you might have touched one of the steps in between! You'll have to do them all over again. . . .' Or, 'I want you to count all the windows and don't dare miss one before you come home.' How horrible, you would say, to encounter in reality a person who imposes such penances on a child. And yet the majority of people (perhaps everybody) carry such a person around, in potential latent form, inside themselves.

There is nothing punitive about obsessive thoughts, however. On the contrary, it is as if something which is not tamed at all welled up in the patient. In fact, they simply express crude unbridled aggression. In the language of psycho-analysis, such thoughts originate in the 'area' of the unconscious which is called the *id*. The compelling thoughts which resemble penances arise from that area of the unconscious which is called the *superego*.

There is a good deal of confusion regarding the nature of the superego in psycho-analytical literature and in text-books. Freud himself was not consistent throughout his life when it came to these concepts which he had created. The triad by which the human person is represented in a schematic diagram (superego, ego, id) may have to be discarded again in a hundred years. Nevertheless, as a diagram which enables us to explain phenomena, it is indispensable. The situation is comparable to that created by the physicist Bohr in his planetary model of the atom. Subsequent studies showed that things were more complicated; yet many discoveries in atomic physics were based on Bohr's concept of a nucleus which corresponds to the sun and electrons which correspond to the planets.

Some of the text-books, particularly some of the popular writings on psycho-analysis, state flatly that the word super-ego is just another word for conscience. Some statements of Freud would lead to the same assumption.

However, consider the examples which we have discussed in this chapter: the girl who is stricken by terror at the idea of eating in the presence of others; the man who is seized by panic while he is 'high up'; the young man who in his dream vision (and in the agony of his waking hours) pays dearly for having rebelled against the father; those who are compelled to go through painful bizarre compulsive rituals. The stage on which all their dramas of fear and penance are played differs from the world of Good and Evil, from the world of virtue and wickedness of which Plato and Aristotle speak, as a nightmare differs from the mild light of day in which the objects of wakeful reality are bathed. One of the keenest and most decisive intuitions of Freud is the fact, so easily discernible in the examples quoted above, that the currents emanating from the primitive superego have much in common with our instinctual drives.

The young lady with the eating phobia does not really expect punishment (as our reason conceives of this idea). To her, it is just a crude, brutal question of eating or being eaten. The compulsive patient does not really undergo penance, as our reason understands the word. He experiences a seemingly irresistible urge which leads to mounting tension. The tension is temporarily relieved when the urge is satisfied but it soon returns like the first pianissimo of a slow crescendo. The eating phobia, the phobia of heights, the compulsive acts all have the earmarks of blind force and of cruelty. With regard to our two phobic patients, I have said that the act of aggression (eating; killing) and the act of atonement (being eaten; falling) penetrate one another. They are interchangeable. They represent drives, except that in the fantasy of atonement the drive is centripetal instead of centrifugal, so to speak: it is a 'drive' all right, but turned against the person himself. We understand why compulsive acts resembling penance, and obsessive thoughts resembling aggression, are so often found in one and the same patient. As we have said, the patient's self resembles a camp fire weakly protected against animals prowling in the dark. But the species of prowlers is irrelevant: the patient cannot resist the urge either to self-punitive or to aggressive thoughts. The famous French psychiatrist Henri Ey objects to the term superego. The prefix 'super,' he says, is misleading. Actually the archaic infantile imagery of punishment is on the same level as the untamed animal of aggressiveness. In his diagram the superego and the id are on the same level. They surround reason on all sides.

What then is the difference between guilt and neurotic guilt? The concept of guilt is closely associated with the concept of justice. Guilt has the quality of proportion.[1] The greater your wrong, the guiltier you are. There is something about this proportion which can almost be quantified. If you find and keep a hundred dollars which belongs to your neighbour, common sense would say that you are much guiltier than if you took a couple of postage stamps from him without returning them. A compulsive-obsessive ('scrupulous') person may feel guiltier for not having returned a couple of postage stamps than a man convicted of the theft of one hundred dollars. Secondly, objective guilt can be assuaged. Like debt, to which it is related, it

[1] As Aristotle has pointed out so beautifully, ethics is related to harmony.

can be paid. Neurotic guilt is insatiable. You cannot appease it. You cannot pay it off. Thirdly, objective guilt does not necessarily depend on emotion. A man may regard himself as guilty and be perfectly relaxed about it. Neurotic guilt is so inextricably interwoven with anxiety, that that which is experienced subjectively is at times only the anxiety without conscious feelings of guilt. Finally (and this is related to point number one) neurotic guilt is related to repressed drives just as much as to realized acts. Objective guilt refers to realized acts only.

All this points in favour of those who draw a clear line between conscience on one hand and the primitive superego on the other. The former is the product of consciousness and the light of reason; the latter is unconscious—it becomes consciously manifest only in a masked form. Conscience has all the characteristics of human reason, primarily those of harmony and of proportion; the superego is originally related to primitive libidinal drives. Conscience is associated with wise self-restraint; the superego is related to blind self-destructiveness. Basically no dread is involved in conscience; the superego, with its element of back-firing aggression, pulsates with anxiety. To be sure, positive elements enter into the formation of the superego at a later stage of the child's development. But conscience contains something which transcends our psychological data.

In a previous chapter we indicated that there is a basic difference between the embryology of the personality as conceived by Freud, and the embryology of the human body as studied by the anatomist. The organs, in their post-uterine shape, have normally lost their embryonic structure once and for all; while psychic functions of the highest order, such as *agape* and conjugal love, seem to retain in a shadowy and latent form all the previous archaic phases of libido, and there is a continuous possibility of regression. Something similar seems to exist as far as the relationship between conscience and superego is concerned, with the possibility of reverting back to archaic levels, and the possibility of a penetration of the archaic into the mature structure.

The cases which I chose to illustrate our argument were somewhat extreme and had a strongly clinical flavour. There are innumerable borderline problems which indicate more clearly the penetration of sub-layers into the area which we call conscience. These are the problems which most urgently need to be taken up by parents, educators, and priests. For example, there is the guilt associated with masturbation. The ideal of chastity is one of those moral truths from which no scientific investigation can take anything away; this is in the nature of things. However, its psychological aspect (what theologians call 'the natural plane') is quite problematic in the light of what we have said. Entirely new vistas open up. All adolescents I have ever seen who were oppressed with anxiety or depression or compulsive rituals on account of masturbation felt that way primarily because of what had happened to them during their first genital phase and only secondarily because of the Jansenist or 'medical' threat. This means that during the phase of early infantile masturbation something happened in these people of which the adolescent anxiety is just a reactivation; the foundation was laid before the advent of reason. Of course, during adolescence a bit of hellfire adds to the anxiety. Although I am opposed to our moral relativists who advocate the abolition of 'sexual taboos' on the basis of scientific discovery, I have much more sympathy with them than with our Jansenist teachers of morality. The former act often out of natural charity while the latter often give vent to neurotic cruelty under the cloak of moral teaching.

Chastity is a lofty ideal. It can be taught only in a positive form, however, well integrated with a teaching of the ideals of charity and justice. Taken out of the context of the Gospel and presented in an isolated form as a conglomerate of *don'ts*, it becomes a diabolical distortion of truth. The medieval poet Langland wrote: 'Chastity without Charity shall be chained in Hell!' Moral nihilists and Jansenists (and there is a surprisingly large number of Catholics whose thinking, particularly on sex, is Jansenistic and basically Manichæan) are brothers-in-arms. Both disfigure the Christian image of man.

This circumstance often forces Christian psychiatrists into a sort of two-front war. In our work we frequently encounter victims of perverted education in matters of sex. Christian morality as it is lived, particularly in the Anglo-Saxon countries, has been predominantly negative during the past few centuries. When we take clinical histories, we always ask questions about religion as a matter of routine. Quite often, in the case of Protestants, the patient will say: 'My father was a good Christian. He never drank or smoked or played cards. . . .' In the case of Catholics, we often have religion outlined in terms of all that has been avoided in the sexual field, such as adultery, birth control, and masturbation. One gets an impression that the Gospel is limited to a list of sexual prohibitions outlined against a frame of eternal fire. It all becomes a matter of *don'ts* which, if done, lead to eternal perdition. Why is there nothing neurotic about the severe asceticism of Saint Don Bosco or Saint Francis of Assisi or Saint John of the Cross? Because their asceticism was, within the hierarchy of the personality, in the place where it belonged. In other words, it was subordinated to charity.

This then seems to be part of the Christian tragedy: guilt reaches into the transcendental above and the temporal-accidental below. Just as love, on the natural plane, has a forerunner in an element of crude possessiveness, the moral idea has a forerunner in an element of dumb fear. Psycho-analytically speaking, every man is his own primitive ancestor. In order to face his guilt in the light of the Gospel, the neurotic has to be freed from the dim, wordless anxiety which is the mark of slavery and which derives from a world without freedom. Neurotic guilt is ancestral. It stems not only from an infantile archaic world; it is not only of the biological order. It keeps us imprisoned in a pre-Christian pagan circle.

In an unredeemed world, guilt is deadweight. All it can do is pull down. In the world of the Gospel, guilt is no longer deadweight; it becomes building material. In Greek tragedy, the guilty man is haunted by the Furies. Guilt is purely of the past, it follows from behind, it does not beckon from in front. It is part of a world of binding necessity, not of free motivation.

When Saint Paul confronts fear and love, he is not merely talking history but he is saying something ontological. In our relationship with Christ, the sense of sin is inseparably associated with love. The Good Thief did not indulge in lengthy self-accusations. He made a simple act of love, and he was answered: 'This day you will be with me in Paradise.' Beyond the region of neurosis, beyond the psychological altogether, the problem of guilt is the problem of love. 'Much is forgiven her, for she has loved much.'

# IX

# Development and Identification

Another human being, as far as he is a person, cannot be a
mere object. There is only one way to participate in another
person—that is to re-live his free acts, in other words to
identify ourselves with his will, his love, and all the rest of him.

MAX SCHELER, *Man's Position in the Cosmos*

The multiform wisdom of God which is set forth lucidly by
Scripture, lies hidden in every cognition and in every nature.
It is also evident that all kinds of knowledge minister to
Theology; and that Theology takes illustrations and uses
phrases pertaining to every kind of knowledge.

ST BONAVENTURE

FREUD, by introducing a genetic principle into his
psychology, unwittingly supplied a lot of material for
a metaphysical concept of man. As we have seen, the
moment one tells a story of unfolding, one implies a
transcendental principle—the entelechy of Aristotle and
Thomas Aquinas.

Those who believe in the primacy of the spirit have still
another reason to be fascinated by this story of formation,
the genetic principle. The question of the formation of
personality in itself has strong moral implications. Consider the *diversity* of character—people as different as
Hamlet and Falstaff, Don Quixote and Sancho Panza,
Alyosha Karamazov and Smerdiakov, Faust and Wagner!
How does character ('a person's moral and mental make-
up') come about?

178

This question can be approached in two ways. One can group people *statically* into certain types and have it over with, or one can attempt *dynamically* to trace the development of traits back to a meeting of two currents: formative forces from within and formative forces from without.

The static attitude is a tacitly assumed premise in many books on characterology. The four classical temperaments (sanguine, melancholic, choleric, and phlegmatic), which played so considerable a role in antiquity and the Middle Ages, formed a static concept. People were pigeon-holed. If in those days one had known the laws of heredity and chromosomes, one would undoubtedly have assumed that temperaments were produced very much as are colours of eyes, skin, and hair. The same attitude is implicit in more recent so-called typologies, such as the one introduced by Kretschmer and later confirmed in a modified form by Sheldon. Kretschmer was struck by the fact that certain forms of insanity do not affect people at random, on the basis of chance occurrence. He found that mentally healthy persons with a certain type of personality are affected, when they become psychotic, by a certain psychosis, those with another type of personality by a different type of psychosis. Thus mankind, instead of being divided into four groups, as of old, was divided into two groups. Though there were complicated subdivisions, the approach was essentially static. Kretschmer's work grew directly out of the development of nosology. It is the approach of the butterfly collector; types are described and labelled. Nevertheless, there is something in Kretschmer's and Sheldon's work which makes it interesting for us in the present context—the correlation between body-build and character. The formative principle which determines the structure of the personality and the formative principle which determines the structure of the body are inter-related. This again is one of the facts which are so obvious to our folklore psychology. Poets have always been aware of it:

> Let me have men about me that are fat;
> Sleek-headed men, and such as sleep o' nights:
> Yond Cassius has a lean and hungry look;
> He thinks too much: such men are dangerous.

It is impossible to visualize Don Quixote as short and stocky, and Sancho Panza as long and thin. It is no coincidence that a systematic interest in this problem arose with Goethe and the characterologists of the Romantic school. It is most remarkable that this trend should form part of a current which reacted against the rationalism of the eighteenth century. The body is not conscious; it forms part of our 'unconscious.' The idea that that which is unconscious should express in its form something psychic is quite alien to the spirit of the eighteenth century. The work of Kretschmer and Sheldon in our century was a scientific step in that Goethean direction. However, even their work, particularly that of Kretschmer, is similar to that of the classical biologist who was mainly interested in description and classification.

It is interesting that all typologies should be so suggestive. No matter how one classifies people, whether into the four categories of antiquity; or the two categories of Kretschmer (schizothymic and cyclothymic); or the two categories of Jung (introvert and extrovert); or many others, one begins to see such types. For this reason it seems easy to establish a new series of types and make them famous. After studying Kretschmer, you find offices or restaurants crowded with Kretschmerian types. After reading Jung, or one of the typologies created by famous educational psychologists, you begin to see their respective types all over the place. You wonder why you never saw them before. The danger in all this pigeon-holing is that it robs the personality of its mystery, of the uniqueness which is wrought in all human development.

Parallel with a static way of looking at human character (the view of the butterfly collector) is the dynamic trend. This is contained in Goethe's expression, *'geprägte Form, die lebend sich entwickelt.'*[1] It is this dynamic approach to the formation of character which attracts the Catholic philosopher. Life with the Gospel and the sacraments implies development. On the natural plane we have to distinguish between two things in the psychology of development. There are *conscious* mechanisms, which are dealt with in works on educational psychology, all the way from Plato to our time. And there are *unconscious* mechanisms. It is here that psycho-analysis has contributed a great wealth of observation. In this connection, we shall deal particularly with the phenomenon of identification, as understood by the psycho-analysts, and the mechanisms related to it.

I have already indicated that the borderlines of the archaic ego are not clearly defined. During the earliest phase of feeding, we are something like an extension of the mother, or the mother is an extension of us. This is the time when, in our fantasy, either the living objects in our surroundings are incorporated and swallowed by us, or we are swallowed and incorporated by them. After all, in the earliest phase of our life the main relationship between us and the world of objects is one of intake and elimination. If you grant the existence of a preverbal, preconceptual world in which the somatic and psychic are still *one*, an

[1] Form imposed, yet livingly evolving.

undissociated and undifferentiated form (and all the facts of observation point at the existence of this world), then you will understand why there is at that stage such an extraordinarily intimate exchange between us and the personalities with whom we are in contact. They become food for our growth, or we become engulfed by them, or we expel them. But the relationship which we have on our conscious, rational, grown-up level—such as choosing our friends, and keeping them at distances graded according to our sympathy—this is not possible. Walter de la Mare's observation on Miss T.,

> *It's a very odd thing,*
> *As odd as can be,*
> *That whatever Miss T. eats*
> *Turns into Miss T.,*

is not necessarily true with regard to our psychic growth— not according to Freud, at least. Here the process is rather reversed. Miss T. turns into that which she eats.

If this is true it means that the mechanism of imitation, which is so important in the formation of the personality and in education generally, is preceded by some sort of archaic forerunner, a process for which the word 'imitation' is misleading because it implies the conscious and intentional. The term 'identification' is much better. Particularly in the early infantile phase the mechanism of identification is on a primitive, vegetative plane—something comparable to biochemical assimilation. Mechanisms of identification which are characteristic of later phases of childhood are more active and are associated with a greater detachment from the object of identification. But even these mechanisms are still quite remote from conscious intentional imitation.

On this basis, Freud's concept of 'pseudo-heredity' becomes understandable. By pseudo-heredity is meant the fact that a resemblance in character between child and parent is not necessarily due to a transmission of traits through chromosomes but may come about in a purely psychic way, i.e., precisely through identification. Proofs of the mechanism of pseudo-heredity are encountered daily in our work. In one of the Social Welfare Agencies there was a woman whose only child, a young man of twenty-three, disappeared without a trace. Seventeen years before, her husband had done the same. Needless to say, she was heartbroken; she did not even know whether her son was still alive. It seemed incredible that this experience should happen under identical circumstances twice in her lifetime! Every psychiatrist has seen several cases of a similar con-stellation of circumstances. It is highly unlikely that there should be a sex-linked quality of 'running-away-from-home-without-a-trace' anchored in the chromosomes, which would manifest itself regardless of outer circumstances. Without further investigation one cannot exclude the fantastic possi-bility of such a mechanical transmission of destinies. But *with* further investigation one finds that everything points in the direction of 'pseudo-heredity' or identification in the sense in which Freud has used these terms.

There are a few noteworthy points about this story. It is obvious that this boy did not sit down at an early age and plan to do what his father did, once he grew up. From other similar situations it is not even likely that he consciously imitated his father's action when he did so, at the age of twenty-three. Moreover, it is likely that the mother unconsciously repeated something in her attitude which prompted the son to run away. He re-enacted a drama, and she may have contributed her role to the re-enactment. In other words, this is not an imitation of the father's action in the sense in which actors re-enact the assassination of Julius Cæsar on the stage. It is much less conscious and planned than that, much less intellectual and arbitrary. There is more of a 'must' in it; it is more 'biological.' Yet it is less biological than if it were really anchored in the chromosomes in such a way that it would have to roll off the tape quite mechanically and independent of outer circumstances, as we see it in certain hereditary illnesses.

Again we have entered a strange layer of the psychic, a realm in which freedom is not the same as in deliberate planning and yet is not excluded as in a machine. Contrary to those processes which are laid down in the chromosomes and roll off the tape, we can *get at* this process of pseudo-hereditary destiny in the psycho-analytic situation and modify it.

To illustrate the meaning of identification in the Freudian sense, we have chosen an example of abnormality because it lends itself exceptionally well to this purpose. The mechanism of identification is just as important, however, for the understanding of the normal growth of the personality. Under normal circumstances the Œdipus conflict is solved by a healthy identification of the boy with the father. The father changes from a rival into a model. In order to attain to the love and admiration of the mother the boy must become like the father. For this reason the boy goes, or rather under normal circumstances should go, through a phase during which he patterns himself after the father. This phase of the father model or father hero replacing the father rival has its greatest significance from around the age of four well into pre-puberty, around the age of twelve.

In girls this development is more complex and less well understood. The original profound maternal identification, or rather undissolved maternal union, through which we all pass is in girls replaced by a phase during which the father is an object of love, the prototype of all masculine love objects which are later to come. After this, also chiefly during the latent phase, the healthy girl should go through a second phase of identification with the mother. Then the mother rival turns into a mother after whom the girl models herself and who helps the girl to accept her womanhood as something positive.

The fact that the original maternal identification is more primitive and archaic, and that later phases of identification stand somehow in between a profound biological fusion on one hand and conscious wilful imitation on the other, is also expressed in the choice of symbols and fantasies, particularly in dreams. A patient who suffered from psycho-neurotic depressions of obscure origin had this repetitive dream: '*I find myself at the end of a wharf and a high wave leaps up behind me to swallow me.*' This woman's mother had gone through much anxiety when the patient was a little less than two years old. Water is an ancient maternal symbol in all cultures. We arise out of the water: ὕδωρ μεν ἄριστον. This is expressed in numerous myths such as the birth of Venus. On the other hand, the maternal principle as something which is threatening to engulf her corresponds to an early phase of our particular patient's existence.

Another patient, a married woman of twenty-nine, was treated for severe psycho-neurotic depressions. The most conspicuous complaint was a deep-seated dread of sexual intercourse. The patient was a healthy, well-developed woman, the wife of a Customs official. They had five

children. The husband was a healthy, seemingly well-adjusted
and considerate man. On the level of objective reality there
was nothing which would account for her sexual maladjustment. One noteworthy feature was the fact that she dreaded
utterly any attempt at preliminary tenderness. If there had
to be sex relations at all, it was better to be taken brutally,
without caressing. It was only under such conditions that
she was at times even able to achieve orgasm. At one phase
of her treatment she reported this dream: '*I am hiding in
the water of a swimming pool before an attacking enemy.
Even though I am in the water the enemy, who is a soldier
in uniform, threatens to set me on fire. He uses a big flame
thrower which sprays a fiery jelly, and in this way the water
catches fire.*

A frequent dynamic principle in cases of this sort is the
fact that the patient, at an early phase, witnesses the sexual
intercourse of the parents. Such an experience to the child
means catastrophic violence. In the child's world such an
event is cataclysmic, brutal, and just the opposite of loving
union. In this example the male partner is a soldier (her
husband wore a Customs official's uniform) whose weapon
is one of brutal destructiveness (the flame-thrower), and
in order to protect herself from it she has to go back into
the pool from which we all come. At the same time that
element of identification explains the imagery. She is identified with the mother-victim. Incidentally her ambivalence
towards that role is quite obvious. In order to be able to
achieve sexual gratification at all, she has to re-enact a
scene of violence.

In both these examples the mother with whom the patient
identifies is symbolized by something which corresponds
to an early ontogenetic image. Moreover, in each of these
two cases the patient *shares the fate* of the mother, she

identifies with a mother *to whom something happens*. Nevertheless it should be noted that the mechanisms are different. In the first case the patient is passively engulfed by something which might destroy her. In the second case the patient dives actively into that same thing—a gesture of hiding from danger, at the same time a gesture by which she becomes subject to danger.

In the case of male juvenile delinquents we not infrequently see that there has never been any wholesome identification with the father, or with any paternal figure. Deep down the patient is still strongly identified with the mother and is simply terrified of that tender core, and fights it with all his might. He becomes destructive and brutal. He 'acts' tough and hard because, deep down, there is no genuine toughness and hardness in him. The best thing which can happen in cases like this is that, while we are working with the patient, he goes through all the vicissitudes of transference, hostility, and love—until he begins to identify with the physician. What happens is a delayed process of something which should have happened before, in the natural setting of the family. In the English language the word 'role' has several meanings. In cases like these juvenile delinquents, the patient actually develops from role-playing towards an acceptance of his role in life.

It should not surprise us to find that the process of identification in the language of the unconscious is often symbolized by the putting on of clothes. A sixteen-year-old girl who had never identified in a positive, healthy way with her mother and who was always in search of her place in life as a woman produced repeatedly during the analysis a dream in which she was choosing clothes in a ladies' store. She would waver between tweed suits on the one hand, and cocktail dresses and evening gowns on the other.

We see in these last examples that the person is no longer suffering, through identification, from what happened to someone else but is actively following someone else's pattern. He is no longer a victim, but a follower; he is no longer being moulded, but he models himself.

It is obvious that a lot of what goes wrong with people is due to what goes wrong with the process of identification. It happens quite frequently that a boy is not able to dissolve his identification with the mother. This may be due to fear of the father, or it may be due to the fact that the father is not close enough to the child. In order to facilitate a strong identification with the father, the latter must be the son's friend. There must be a meeting on a level in between; the father must share the boy's interests during the latent phase; he must stoop so that the boy can stretch himself. The mother herself must have a certain degree of love and natural admiration for the father to facilitate such a paternal identification on the part of her son. There are a great number of variables in this mechanism and therefore it is not surprising that many different things often go wrong with it. If the maternal identification is maintained too strongly, the element of femininity is too strongly emphasized in the son's personality. This is one of the elements which contribute to the genesis of homosexuality.

The same holds true with reference to girls. If the mother, for any number of reasons, should not lend herself to a healthy identification, the girl is unable to resolve her 'Electra complex' and identifies too strongly with the father. In the case of conscious hostility against the parent of the same sex, an irrational hostility which is carried into the later phases of childhood and into adolescence, one speaks of an unresolved 'Œdipus conflict' or 'Electra conflict.' In such a case the pattern of negative identification may be established. The child develops traits which are precisely the opposite of the traits of the parent who is the object of hostility. In the end the child's personality is related to that of the parent as a negative film is related to a photograph. If the father is a spendthrift, the son becomes a miser, and vice versa; the daughter of a mother with Victorian and puritanical background becomes as promiscuous as a prostitute. Usually these people do not enjoy their state of rebellion at all. Apart from other mechanisms, which I do not want to discuss in this connection, mechanisms which are associated with incestuous desire and guilt, there is this mechanism of negative identification. Out of hostility arises an image which is the complete negation of the mother. The combination of Victorianism and puritanism does not represent purity in the sense in which Christians understood it. There is frequently nothing but an unhealthy form of repression. The daughter lives that which the mother has so inadequately repressed.

We have seen that the process of identification begins before there is any rational understanding or verbal communication. The child seems to be close to that pre-verbal world for a long time, even after speech and rational understanding have developed. He is closer to it, at any rate, than we grown-ups are. This explains why that which is never expressed in words influences the formation of character as much as that which is expressed. In unhappy marriages it often happens that parents make a point of keeping their conflict from the children: there is never any row in front of them; tragedy is carefully kept hidden. Nevertheless, when children from such marriages are later analysed, they reveal unconscious material which corresponds exactly to that which has been kept from them. In such cases the child's unconscious is the cupboard which contains the parents' skeleton.

The trouble is that, in the world of our infantile ego, there is something like a law of 'all or none.' To us grown-ups there are very clear gradations of hostility: some unhappy marriages are less unhappy than others. The child's dim, prehistoric experience of hostility is frequently bizarre, blown-up and distorted. There are two huge troglo-dytic images—one of an aggressor and one of a victim. Both images are over-lifesize, and have an all-out quality, perhaps more so the earlier the imprint is made. A lot of the sadistic pattern with which some people walk through life is caused by the aggressor whom they have 'taken in' at an early phase. A lot of the masochistic pattern of others is due to the fact that they are permanently identified with the victim.

To what extent does a child really identify himself with what he grasps intellectually in the image of a person? To what extent do those features enter which lie underneath the threshold of rational understanding—all that which is lived, but not communicated? These are questions difficult to answer in any given case. Some years ago a young man of eighteen was treated who presented the classical picture of the so-called 'a-social psychopath.' He played the role of a big shot, and in order to attain this purpose he swindled, embezzled, forged cheques and travelled under assumed high-sounding names. His a-social pattern was quite primi-tive. He was a messenger boy for a big store and, when sent on errands for which he had to be given cash, he would use it for his own purposes. When he was sent to get sleeping-car reservations for one of his bosses, he stopped at a famous hotel, took a suite of rooms, posed as the representative of a well-known New York firm (he looked considerably older than his age and, like so many of his kind, cut a good figure) and invited girls up to his suite. There he had lavish sessions with champagne and the rest. When all the cash was spent, he would forge cheques. This boy had considerable insight and even something like remorse. However, his insight did not prevent him from relapsing time and again.

He came, like many patients of this category, from a good family. He was the youngest of five. There was nothing wrong with his brothers and sisters. They all were respectable people and had found their station in life. The patient was a late-comer. There was a difference of seven years between him and the second youngest. The father was a consulting engineer who at one time had occupied an excellent position with a fabulous income. However, at one point in the family history the father had suffered a tragic crash and lost all his money. After that he tried hard to make a come-back and, in order to achieve this, carefully maintained a social façade. He kept up his office at the same 'good address' and in the same grand style. He maintained all his club memberships and had lunch at the same places as before—all this with the aid of loans from relatives. The idea was that he could regain his original economic position if he did not lose face socially; he was compelled to keep up an entirely false front.

Our young patient was four years old when the crash happened. During my frequent contacts with him, it became increasingly apparent that this factor had been most decisive in his development. In contrast to the four older children, he had grown up with a father who lived a life of make-believe. One might perhaps best express it by saying that this boy did not identify himself with a person but with a role. The entire thing was intimately associated with the

Œdipus conflict. It is remarkable that the father was an unshakable optimist who year after year saw 'the big comeback' just around the corner. The mother seemed to bear all the worries of those years. The only dream the patient ever reported during our several years of contact was the following: '*I meet a poor girl who lives in dismal slumlike surroundings, and I buy her a palatial house in the best residential district.*' It is interesting that, in relating this dream, he associated the luxurious house with the actual home of a well-known gambler.

In this boy's father there existed a marked discrepancy between the person's social role and the true person. This play-acting was bound to have a bad effect on the son's development. Such a rift between outer appearance and inner character exists in many of us. Many psychologists have made a distinction between 'social ego' and ego proper, between 'role' and person. Jung called the social ego *persona* in contrast to personality. The word *persona* is derived from the concept of the mask. The actors on the stage of ancient Rome wore masks with mouthpieces through which the words sounded (*per-sonare*). The person in his social role is often quite different from the person as he appears in his intimate life. Many people become more dependent on their own *persona*. Their social ego, their role as bank president or railway guard, has the same function as the exterior skeleton in crustaceæ. They are so united to their social ideal that they would collapse, and very little would remain, if one robbed them of their position in society. Children's growing selves are quite sensitive to this discrepancy. By a number of factors they become identified with social ideals rather than with human beings of flesh and blood.

Tragic examples of this were encountered in our work

in an Old Age Counselling Service which was run in association with social welfare agencies. We saw old ladies
emerging from the poorest downtown rooming areas of
Montreal, speaking and moving in the manner of the
Edwardian drawing-room, lavender scent and all. One
elderly bachelor appeared with double-breasted suit, wore
his pince-nez attached to a black cord, and addressed me
in a peculiarly stilted manner. Two days after the first
interview, I received a letter indicating his address in a
manner which somehow succeeded in imitating the formal
letterheads of the upper-class society of his childhood days.
He indicated to me in a few lines how pleased he was to
have obtained insight into my work—the sort of note the
Governor-General of Canada might have written. This
man, who was on the point of starvation, came from a
family which forty years before had been close to the Prime
Minister, and which entertained on Sunday afternoons in
their home a young student who himself was later to
become Prime Minister.

My first impression on encountering these people was
that I was dealing with what is called 'genteel poverty.' I
felt that they over-emphasized their higher social origin
because of the humiliating situation of receiving 'charity,'
and hence the lavender scent and the formal letters of
acknowledgement. On studying these cases more closely,
however, I discovered that the situation was almost the
reverse: they did not re-enact the Edwardian drawing-
room because they received public assistance—they had
become recipients of public assistance because they kept
up the Edwardian drawing-room. It could be shown in
every one of these cases that quite early in childhood the
person had identified himself strongly with the *persona*,
the social role and the social ideals of a parent, that his

entire attitude towards life had become unrealistic or, it might be better said, un-real. It was exceedingly difficult to approach these clients psycho-therapeutically, not only because of their advanced age but because it was well-nigh impossible to penetrate the mask and meet the human being. They were culturally displaced persons; one had the feeling of encountering petrifactions.

During the process of identification children absorb, as if by osmosis, our sense of values. If our scale of values is that of an external hierarchy, our children cannot grow. Nobody can grow on synthetic stuff. Saint John of the Cross said that 'ambition in the hierarchy is an abomination before God,' and this applies not only to ecclesiastical hierarchy but to social hierarchies in general.

The importance of the good example and model in education has always been known. The new vista opened up by psycho-analysis is the mechanism by which that which is not expressed in words communicates itself. Here is something like an embryology of learning; a scale that reaches from the quasi-mystic participation of the infant in the person of the mother into later phases, in which that which is not spoken and even withheld or disguised is nevertheless effective; a dynamic interchange between parent and child which reaches very far beyond the borders of consciousness.

Freud has remarked how baffling it is to see patients go through life relentlessly haunted by a cruel, punitive super-ego while it is clear that their parents were anything but cruel or over-demanding. In these cases, he claimed, it can be shown that the parents themselves had a powerful, morbid superego. This element did not overtly enter into the up-bringing of the children. Nevertheless the child adopts, as if by silent agreement, that part of the parent's personality.

A lady of sixty-three was treated for a serious state of melancholia. She suffered from bizarre delusions of guilt. She was convinced she was condemned to eternal perdition because of 'impure thoughts.' Some time before she had acutely broken down, she had developed involved compulsive rituals which forced her to go on praying all night until she was exhausted and fell asleep in the morning. Like so many patients of this kind, she paced restlessly up and down the ward and would speak of nothing but hellfire. The most pertinent fact about her childhood history was the loss of her mother in early infancy. The father did not remarry. She described him as a gentle, mild-mannered man who was 'very kind' to her. The only distinct episode of her childhood she remembered was a remark made by her father about the question of getting remarried: he felt that, if he remarried, he might bring misfortune to the family. From the way she put it, it was obvious that he did not mean that he might be marrying the wrong woman. He was actually expressing some dark and sinister prophecy that anything which would make life easier for him would inevitably be followed by disaster. It was precisely this element, and not the kind and loving care of her father, which threatened to destroy her when the forces of her own ego had grown weak.

Thus far we have dealt with the unconscious process of identification only in one direction. In all these episodes, it is the 'I' who identified himself with someone. It would need an entire chapter to describe the way in which we unconsciously identify others with others—with persons who at one time, usually in early childhood, played an eminent role in our lives. Compared with the objective reality in which we adults live, the persons of our early life are overcharged with emotional significance. They are larger than lifesize. And they have the peculiar property of being able to *stain* the image of persons whom we encounter subsequently. Anyone who has acquired a little knowledge of psycho-analysis, particularly through the reading of popular treatises, knows that a man's choice of a wife is influenced by the character of his mother, his sister, or any woman who was prominent in his childhood. Naturally the same thing holds true with reference to a woman's choice of a husband and her early relationships to male figures. No case of irrational hostility in marriage could be explained without the psycho-analytical theory of inter-personal relationship. It is as if the earliest human figures who surrounded us had been endowed with such affective power that it lasts for a lifetime.

A great deal of our work consists of difficulties of inter-personal relationships—difficulties at work with superiors or with co-workers; or difficulties in the family with one's marital partner or with one's children. Many of these difficulties are not based on the actual data of the objective situation; they are of a neurotic nature. Or they are partly based on the objective situation but they are endowed by the patient with an extra something which is not really there. For example, in the office the boss may be difficult to get along with. But for some peculiar reason the employee, who has to endure this difficulty, seems neither able to dissolve or surmount the relationship nor to stand it. He cracks under it. He has brought a problem of his own into the relationship. Without the employee's knowledge, the boss becomes a figure stained with an affective dye which the employee has carried over from somebody else. He is part of what some German psycho-analysts call the 'nest situation.' And all figures of the nest situation are *dramatis personæ par excellence*. We meet them again and again in the most clever disguises. The word 'identification' is possibly wrong in this connection; it might be better to speak of 'transference,' if this term were not associated with the therapeutic situation.

Thus we see how identification enters into development; the subtle currents by which conscious and unconscious penetrate one another; the analogy which exists between somatic forms and those forms which are psychic, but not conscious; the extension of the laws of organic growth and the laws of assimilation far beyond the limits of consciousness, into the unfolding of the highest form—the person.

Let us assume that the psycho-analytical observations about the development of the personality are correct; that there really exists an archaic ego which is intertwined with the body image in a way difficult for grown-ups to define; that there is an early form of identification which is nothing but oral incorporation; that, even later, more mature forms of identification are still related to this psycho-physical unit; that identification is something simpler and more intimate, less intellectual and more immediate than intentional imitation.

If all these observations are correct, then Christian philosophy has found support from a most unlikely ally. The entire concept is quite strange to us modern people. We think much too mechanistically. It would not be strange at all to a person brought up in an Aristotelian-Thomist tradition. It presupposes the living idea of a unit of body and mind from which we have become quite alienated by the development of the last few centuries. Of all the psychological systems, this is the one which approximates most closely a parallel to things which are actually of an ontological order. This explains what we have already observed:

when logical positivists and dialectical materialists deal with psychology, they have a preference for Pavlov or for behaviourism. There is no danger that the Holy Ghost will ever dwell in a machine.

In psycho-analytic theory, things are not so mechanistic even when they seem so. For example, in psycho-analytic articles on religion the observation is often made that Holy Communion is an act of oral incorporation. Usually this is stated in such an aggressive vein of nineteenth-century Knowing-Better-Than-You, that the apparently debunked Christian asks himself timidly: 'Is it true? Holy Communion just oral incorporation?' In a way, it certainly is. As I have mentioned, contrary to the mechanism of organic nutrition, during the process of (identification by) oral incorporation, as Freud first observed it, the child turns into that which it takes in. St Leo says: 'Participation in the Body and Blood of Christ produces in us no other effect than to make us pass into that which we take' (Sermon 63 De Passione Domini 12, c.7 PL 54,357). Saint Thomas says:

> Corporal food is first converted into him who eats it, and through this conversion it repairs the losses of the organism and gives it the necessary increase. But the Eucharistic food, instead of being transformed into the one who takes it, transforms him into Itself. It follows that the proper effect of the Sacrament is to transform us so much into Christ that we can truly say: 'I live, now not I, but Christ liveth in me.' (In *Sent.*, Lib. IV, dist. xii, qu.2, a.1, qu${}^a$1.)

Other writers use a language which may sound revolting to some people—for example, Saint Francis of Sales:[1]

> But what do you understand by spiritual digestions of Jesus Christ? Those who digest material food will feel a new vigour through their whole body, by the general distribution

[1] *Meditations on the Love of God.*

which is made through it. So those who digest well spiritually, feel that Jesus Christ who is their food, diffuses and communicates himself to all the parts of their soul and body. They have Jesus Christ in their brain, in their heart, lungs, eyes, hands, tongues, ears and feet. But this Saviour, what does he, thus circulating everywhere? He straightens all, he purifies all, he mortifies all, he vivifies all, he loves in the heart, he understands in the brain, he breathes in the lungs, he sees in the eyes, he hears in the ears, and so of the rest.

This feeling of revulsion is nothing new. It is not, as one might think, due to the fact that we live in a scientific age. It is indicated in one of the most dramatic episodes of the New Testament. When Jesus said, 'For my flesh is meat indeed, and my blood is drink indeed. He that eats my flesh and drinks my blood, abides in me and I in him' (John vi, 56–57), He knew that 'his disciples murmured at him' and He asked, 'Does this scandalize you?' It did. Many of them 'went back and walked no more with him' (vi, 67).

The appalling idea occurs that it might be thought that I am attempting to 'explain scientifically' something which is of the supernatural order. I should feel like one of those nineteenth-century professors who wanted to 'rescue' revealed religion by explaining the appearance of manna in the desert on the basis of the latest discoveries in biology and meteorology. What is being attempted here is actually the opposite. It means that depth psychology approaches areas in which it becomes difficult to discern the psychological from the ontological, areas in which all analogies become mysterious and impenetrable.

The same people who have discovered that the most archaic form of identification is that of oral incorporation tell us that belief in the Holy Eucharist is a sign of infantile regression. It is, if they mean child-likeness in its vastest, metaphysical sense. Christians accept this on the highest authority. 'Unless you are converted to little children, you cannot enter the kingdom of Heaven.' 'Unless a man be born again, he cannot see the kingdom of God.' The sacramental life follows, as Saint Thomas pointed out, all the various phases of growth as we know them from the natural order. What is true about the sacramental life is true about spirituality in general. In later phases the process of identification, as I have said, is quite different from conscious, intentional imitation. There is profound need for a model. We cannot grow without a trellis. This mechanism is removed from the intimacy of oral incorporation, yet it occurs on a deep level. The dream of the child who tried on many clothes is a frequently occurring pattern. We are in search of a person to put on. But there is an important difference from the role of the actor. We *become* that which we put on.

It almost seems as if Saint Paul knew about the symbols of the unconscious. He speaks of 'putting on' Christ. This phase of identification is no less real than the Eucharistic one. It is hard for us ordinary people to realize what it means 'to put on' Christ. But we get an idea from the lives of the saints. Incidentally, there is one remarkable feature about this form of identification. Don Bosco was surrounded by children. Saint John of the Cross lived in the night of Gethsemane. Saint Benedict Joseph Labre had no place to rest his head. It is as if each Saint chose one facet of a huge image. We cannot quite think of Saint John of the Cross spending his life with children, or Don Bosco remaining in contemplative solitude. Their gifts were diverse. In this respect we see again that Grace builds on Nature.

At any rate, whether we think of Christ in the sacramental life or of Christ as *causa exemplaris*, the main point of our argument is this: there exists a remarkable analogy between two mechanisms of *becoming*. What depth psychology has discovered about the laws of growth on the natural plane bears an uncanny resemblance to the laws of growth as they have been known on the spiritual plane. Of course, the idea that the supernatural is analogous to the natural is not new. Only here it is applied to a new set of observations. If God wanted to communicate with Man, it is reasonable to think that He would choose those channels which are most intimate to us, that He would bend down to reach us at the simplest yet deepest level.

Without being aware of it, people meet figures from the scenes of their childhood all their lives.[1] I have been dealing for a long time with a patient who kept changing his working places because there was no boss with whom he was able to get along. Although some of his employers may have been bad people, it was unlikely on the basis of mathematical chance that they all were that bad. It did not take long to find out that the patient was in the habit of coming across his deceased father in the cleverest and most unlikely disguises—as a plant manager who bellowed at him over the phone, as the chief editor of a newspaper who refused to give him a rise when he thought he deserved one, as a merchant for whom he kept books. All his reactions to these employers were strangely violent, infinitely more so than the situation warranted. He did not know it, but he saw one man behind the mask of all those men: that man was his father. This sort of thing is so very common that one is almost inclined to think that it is the bizarre distortion of something which in itself is normal.

[1] In psycho-analytic literature the term 'identification' is not applied to this mechanism.

The theologian is not surprised at this, because it has an eminently normal yet supernatural counterpart. It has a meaning in the process of salvation. Our Lord has indicated frequently that any human being who is in need of love is Himself dressed up for the occasion. 'Whatsoever you have done to the least of my brethren, you have done unto me. . . .' 'I have been hungry, and you have fed me. . . .' 'Whoever says that he loves God and hates his brother is a liar. How can he love God whom he does not see, if he does not love his brother whom he sees?' Just as our disturbed employee beamed hostility, which had actually been aimed at his father, towards his superiors throughout his life, we are asked to beam the love we have for God to anyone whom we happen to come across, to our neighbour.

The latter process does not need to be conscious. Whatever you have done to the least of His brethren, whether you knew it or not, you have done unto Him. In psychoanalytical terms, Christ points at Himself in the *causa exemplaris* as one object of identification, and in the least of our brethren as another object of identification. In the first case, you identify yourself with Him; in the second case, you identify someone beside yourself with Him.

# X

# Psychiatry and the Life of the Spirit : I

But the foolish things of the world hath God chosen, that
He may confound the wise; and the weak things of the world
hath God chosen, that He may confound the strong.

I CORINTHIANS 1: 27

A T least once each year during our clinical conferences,
a student brings up this question: 'You say that this
patient suffers from a schizophrenic process, and
one of the symptoms you point out is the fact that he hears
voices. What about Saint Teresa of Avila or the Prophet
Ezekiel? They heard voices and had visions. Why do you
not regard them as psychotic?' There are several things one
can say to elucidate the problem on the natural plane. As
in all these questions there exists no pat, mathematical
solution. There will always be a gap which only faith can
fill. To begin with one can say that two psychic phenomena
can belong to the same category, and yet one be normal and
the other pathological. They are *phenomenologically* the
same but, within their respective contexts, they have two
entirely opposite values. At one time the composer Zelter,
the friend of Goethe, spread the rumour that Beethoven
had gone insane. One of the reasons for this was that
Beethoven, after the 'Hammerklavier' Sonata had gone to
the printer, sent a message to his publisher stating that he

would like to add one bar, consisting of two chords, to the slow movement. This bar was to be added at the beginning, preceding the first bar of the original version. The slow movement of that particular sonata is one of the longest movements in musical literature; that anyone could, as an afterthought, wish to add one more bar to this huge structure (and with definite signs of anxiety) must have appeared mad indeed. At another time Beethoven implored his publisher to add two staccato dots to something already in print. Gustave Flaubert, a master of prose, on one occasion found that an adjective was not quite adequate to convey accurately his shade of meaning (in this case the colour of a beetle) and he changed the word. After that he found the sentence somewhat out of balance, changed other words, and ended up by rewriting several preceding pages.

Phenomenologically, as far as the objective observer can see, this is compulsive behaviour. If a civil servant or a business man showed such a pattern in his work it might seriously impair his efficiency, and we might be inclined to regard him as a maladjusted person. Flaubert suffered from epilepsy. There are some experienced clinicians—for example, Bleuler—who claim that compulsiveness is frequently found in the working pattern of so-called idiopathic epileptic patients. I have seen two epileptic patients, on different occasions, who worked on ship models in an occupational therapy class. Neither of them ever quite finished his model. The models looked finished to all intents and purposes, but the patient could still see some flaw, a little bit to be done here or there, a little touch which somehow never was the final one. Dostoievsky, another great epileptic, wrote a novel of about two thousand pages to describe the events of a few days, and his notes, discovered after his death, showed that this novel was conceived only as an introduction to the real one which never came about.

If we applied to the actions of creative artists the word 'compulsive' it would be quite meaningless clinically. A mechanism which might signify a serious character disturbance if we encountered it in the business of everyday life has achieved an entirely different meaning rediscovered in this different setting, the creative process.

To go one step further, there are reliable witnesses who tell us that Mozart heard his works, before he composed them. He not only heard them in the way most composers hear before or while they write. He heard all the physical qualities as well—strings, woodwinds, brasses, and so on. He wrote down what he heard. If that is true, and from Mozart's creative pattern it might well be true, he was hallucinated. A hallucination is the 'sensory perception of an object which is not present.' If he was hallucinated, was he a sick man? Nobody would call Mozart's symphonies the creations of a sick mind, even if it were historically proved that he heard them with all the qualities of acoustic perception, as our psychotic patients hear voices. Thus we see that something which is phenomenologically abnormal (to be hallucinated is not the norm) is not necessarily pathological. It may be supra-normal, above the norm. There are other features which distinguish Mozart from an insane man: he was remarkably well integrated in his environment; none of his actions was 'crazy.' Moreover, the things which he did hear were significant and beautiful to a great number of people, though perhaps not to everybody. He did not insist that what he heard could be heard by everybody else, nor did the mystics. For example, it can be said about Saint Teresa that she was, apart from her supranatural experiences, a practical woman with a sense of humour, quite different from a schizophrenic. And so were many other geniuses of art and the life of the spirit. All this shows that a person can see things or hear things which nobody else sees or hears, and yet be healthy—or even 'healthier' than most of us; the word 'health' is etymologically related to 'whole' and to 'holy.'

Nevertheless there always remains an element of madness in the spiritual encounter. Just think of Abraham, the father of Faith. What would happen today if a man took his son to the summit of a mountain in order to kill him as a sacrifice to God? No matter how much he tried to persuade us that God had told him to do so, we would not hesitate for a moment to treat him as insane. Whenever in the history of revelation man and God meet face to face, as it were, something happens which is not at all normal. This is the sign of paradox which marks the entire story of revelation. Unlike the God of the philosophers, who is an object of demonstration, the God of revelation in His relationship with man does not proceed *more geometrico;* it is a relationship of love. God loves man with the madness of love, and He tries man's love to the point of madness. It is only in this way that we can understand the story of a jealous, angry God of the Old Testament, a God who chooses one particular people from other peoples; a God of whom Abraham is an archetype—yet He really did sacrifice His only Son. It is a mad story, and those who get involved must be affected by divine madness. 'God is a devouring fire.'

Think what would happen today if a man undressed in the public square, as Saint Francis of Assisi did, and flung his clothes in his father's face. Or consider Saint Benedict Joseph Labre, who actually never did what we call 'useful work.' He was refused entry into religious communities.

For the greater part of his life he migrated on the highways of Europe from one place of pilgrimage to another. He embraced a peculiar form of poverty, sleeping under bridges and in doorways, living off people's refuse. Most of the time he was unkempt, unclean and covered with vermin. Today there would be a big file about him in one of the Social Welfare agencies; there would be 'personality tests,' and he would be classified in category E by army physicians. When it comes to the life of the spirit, our concept of the normal breaks down because it is a concept of conformity, of the *juste milieu*.

In this connection it is quite understandable why Kierke-gaard was so deeply affected by the image of Abraham's sacrifice. Protestantism in the early nineteenth century seemed to him to have become almost a routine religion of respectable people. Protestant writers such as Schleier-macher expressed the romantic mood of the time and 'religion' was often not much more than the feelings you have when you look at overwhelmingly beautiful scenery, such as sunset. One can be moved by scenery and one can like it—but one cannot love it as a man loves his mother or his wife or his child. One cannot be deeply, irrevocably committed to it. The quixotic element, the craziness, is missing. That element is what Kierkegaard saw in the story of Abraham. This is what he postulated in a living relation-ship with God. It is a total abandoning, a foolish surrender —from man to God and God to man. The saints move out-side the *juste milieu* and belong to what well-integrated bourgeois people call the 'lunatic fringe.'

Thus we see that clinical concepts which refer to reason and order in the practical things of everyday life lose their significance when we enter the life of the spirit. We have indicated in other places that psychiatry and psycho-analysis are unable to penetrate into the mystery of the Person. Nowhere does this become as apparent as in connection with the supernatural life. The natural sciences and technology occupy themselves with problems; the classical descriptive psychiatrist of the nineteenth century labelled and pigeon-holed human beings; the experimental psychologist tests his subject and symbolizes functions in a graph; the psycho-analyst uses a dynamic formula. And all the while the contours of each single human person are far outside the range of comprehension, imperceptibly dissolving into something which is of the metaphysical order.

We have seen that the psycho-analytic approach is more related to a Christian concept of the human person and more akin to the movement of charity than other psychological methods. Yet when we approach the range of divine folly, the clinical formula fails. And this is a good thing. Man would cease to be man if there were not altitudes of existence in which the distribution of elements is changed and the cosmic rays are more powerful, so that our ordinary instruments are out of working order.

Sainte Theresa of Lisieux, who was deeply attached to her father, received the news that he was afflicted by an illness which entailed much suffering. She stated later that these were the happiest days of her life. By common standards that is a mad statement. It is easy, almost too easy, to apply the formula. Words offer themselves freely, words like 'masochistic,' 'identification,' and so on. And on the natural plane these terms are probably quite in order to 'describe the mechanism,' as we say if we look at it isolated from the entire context. But in isolating that which is of the natural order we obtain an artifact, something which does not at all describe reality. It is appallingly insufficient.

Sainte Angela de Foligno was a married noblewoman,

the mother of several children. She lived a carefree, apparently quite promiscuous life. She lost her husband and her children. After that she embraced a life of penitence, and went through the most extraordinary mystic states associated with terrifying 'temptations.' On one occasion, we are told, she 'burned her flesh.' She adopted a life of voluntary poverty and had a large following of people who worked with her in caring for the sick and the poor. Her influence on her surroundings was apparently extraordinary. After two years of inner torment, of a kind which is the earmark of the mystical life, she attained a high state of mystical elevation, and her statements on prayer, and on the love and beauty of God, belong to the best of mystical literature. What she went through before she got there is described in words which are shocking and scandalizing to any modern reader, regardless of his clinical experience or lack of it:

In order, therefore, that I might not feel myself exalted by the magnitude and the number of the revelations, visions, and conversings with God, and that I might not be puffed up with the delight thereof, the great tempter was sent unto me, who did afflict me with many and divers temptations, wherefore was I afflicted both in my soul and in my body. The torments of the body were verily numberless and were administered by many demons in divers ways, so that I do scarce believe that the sufferings and infirmity of my body could be written down. There remained not one of my members the which was not grievously tormented; neither was I ever without pain, without infirmity, or without weariness. Always was I weak and feeble, and full of pain, so that I was compelled to be almost continually lying down. All my limbs were as though beaten, and with many troubles did the demons afflict me. Thus was I perpetually sick and swelled, and in all my limbs I did suffer pain, so that it was difficult for me to move myself. Nevertheless, was I not weary of lying still, neither was I yet able to eat sufficient. In short, the sufferings of the body were great, but those of the soul were beyond all comparison, more bitter and more numerous, and all were inflicted by the same demons. I can only liken myself unto one who is hanged by the neck, his hands tied behind his back and his eyes bound, and who is left hanging by a rope upon the gallows; and although he hath no help or remedy or support, he doth, nevertheless, continue to live in that even torment and cannot die. And I do affirm that even more desperately, and with greater cruelty was I afflicted by demons, for they hanged my soul and all its strength was overwhelmed and departed from it. And seeing how that I had no power to oppose them, my grief was so great that at times I was scarce able to weep for rage and for grievous suffering. Moreover, I wept without obtaining relief, and oft-times was my rage so great that I could scarce refrain from rending myself and beating myself most grievously, thus causing my head and all my members to swell. When my soul beheld itself cast down and all its virtue departed from it, then it made great lamentation, and then did I cry unto my God.

After this I did endure another torment, for every vice was reawakened within me. Not that—albeit reawakened —they had power to overcome my reason, but they did occasion me much tribulation. And not only did I remember those vices which assailed me in times past, but many others which I did never before know entered into my body and did inflame me and cause me the utmost suffering. But because they had no lasting power over me they did afford me great consolation when they began to weaken and leave me. This was the work of the demons into whose hands I perceived I had been delivered, but when I do remember how that God was afflicted here below and in poverty, I would that mine own sufferings might be increased twofold.

At times was I thrown into a most horrible darkness of spirit by the demons, wherein it did appear that all hope of good was withdrawn from me. Then those vices which were dead inwardly in the soul were revived outwardly in the body, both those which I did never before feel, and those which I did have aforetimes. And I did suffer so greatly that I was constrained to put actual fire upon my body in order that it might quench the burning of desire; and this I did continue to do until my confessor forbade me. And when I was in that darkness of spirit methought I would have chosen rather to be roasted than to endure such pains. Wherefore did I cry aloud and call upon death, desiring that it should come in any form whatsoever if only God would permit me to die. And unto God did I say: 'Lord, if Thou wilt send me into hell, I pray Thee tarry not, but do it instantly, and since Thou hast abandoned me, make an end of it now and plunge me into the depths.' Presently I perceived that this was the work of demons and that such vices exist not in the soul, for never would I have consented thereto. Howsoever, the body doth suffer violence, and so great is the grief and pain that if it should endure the body would not be able to bear it. Moreover, the soul doth find that all its strength hath been taken from it, and albeit it doth in no wise consent unto vice, yet can it not resist. And seeing that it doth act contrary to the will of God, it loseth all hope of being able to resist and is tormented by those vices.

Among others, God did permit one vice to enter into me the which I had never before known, but I did clearly perceive that it entered into me by Divine permission, and it was so great that it did exceed all others. Upon the other hand was there given unto me a certain virtue, manifestly wherewith to oppose the aforesaid vice and by means of which God did most potently set me free. Wherefore even if I had not already possessed a sure faith in God, this one thing alone would have inspired me with such a faith and a certain hope, of the which I could in no wise doubt. For virtue did increase and vice did diminish, and I was so upheld by that virtue that I could not consent unto wrongdoing, and likewise by means of that virtue was I so enlightened and strengthened that not all the men who were in the world, nor all the demons, could have persuaded me to commit the smallest sin. Hence proceedeth the aforesaid faith in God. The aforesaid vice was so great that I am ashamed to speak of it, and of such potency that if the virtue had tarried in coming to

succour me, neither shame nor suffering nor anything whatsoever would have sufficed to restrain me from instantly
falling back into sin. And all this did I bear for the space of
more than two years.[1]

Subtract the world of Grace from all this, and nothing
but neurosis remains. In that respect there exists a parallel
between the mystic and the creative artist, except that the
mystic goes through a process in which the flesh, the bones,
the sinews, the nerves are even more exposed than in the
life of the artist. It is almost too tempting not to wheel the
psychological microscope into focus. Yet what would we
attain by it? It is, as Jung once said, like attempting a
description of Cologne Cathedral by examining its stones
chemically. Nowhere does Pascal's antithesis of the great-
ness and misery of man come out as poignantly as when
we look, with the chemist's eye, at the psychological humus
from which sanctity grows. If there were nothing beyond
the psychological, all the saints from Simeon Stylites to the
Poverello, to Benedict Joseph Labre, to Thérèse of Lisieux,
would indeed make up a fools' parade. Yet there is no area
in which the 'nothing but,' the reductive principle, is more
absurd than the life of the spirit. Under that aspect the
spirit evaporates, and life itself becomes reduced to a
desiccated specimen.

Pascal has said: 'Knowledge has two end points which
touch one another: one is the pure, natural ignorance which
all men have when they come into this world. At the other
end are the great men who, after having traversed all
human knowledge, know that they do not know, and who
come back to their original state of ignorance; this, however, is a knowing ignorance, an ignorance which looks

[1] From *An Anthology of Mysticism*, ed. by Paul de Jaegher, S.J. The
Newman Press, Westminster, Maryland, 1950.

through itself. Those who have abandoned the first state of ignorance, and never reached the second one, have a varnish of saturated wisdom. They play the role of the initiated ones. They are the people who obscure the world. Their judgment is falser than anybody else's.' These words are so appropriate whenever one comes across a study in which something which is of the supernatural order is boiled down to its psychological substrate. With a few exceptions, most psycho-analytic studies which deal with the supernatural bear that stigma. Nevertheless, we have to admit one thing: the psychological plane and the spiritual plane are not independent of each other. On the contrary, they are most intimately connected.

Consider the following example. Helene Deutsch[1] in discussing Saint Bernadette Soubirous, observes why little Bernadette came to see the 'Lady,' at the time of her original vision. She analyses little Bernadette's relationship to her mother, to the remaining children of the family, the actual situation on the day of the first apparition, particularly the role of Bernadette's sister who had waded across the river before Bernadette. Finally the psycho-analyst speaks of the symbolic significance of the cold rushing river and the 'Lady.' One can say, as Helene Deutsch does, that the child's inner constellation was such that at that moment she had to produce a hallucinatory Great Mother. This psycho-analytic interpretation is probably quite correct, though it says nothing about the question of the reality of the apparition. If nothing exists beyond the psychological, it is the only possible explanation. If something else does exist, as every Christian believes, there is another explanation: suppose the Blessed Virgin were to choose a certain time and place to appear, would she not choose a girl who

---

[1] Helene Deutsch, *The Psychology of Women*. Grune & Stratton, 1948.

was, on the natural plane, best prepared for the encounter? Would she not choose someone whose psychological constellation was such that it offered a natural response? One has to be 'hungry' to be filled by God 'with good things' (Luke i, 53). 'I have to decrease so that you may increase.' This is a principle which one can discover at every step along the history of salvation. The election did not go to the mighty Egyptians, but to a little tribe of slaves—just the sort of people who might have dreamed up the story of special election—it is the sort of myth you would expect them to come up with, as a 'compensation' for their humiliation. And so it goes, all the way down to the weak and enslaved people of the Roman imperial time who, according to Nietzsche, had to invent a shackled and suffering God in order to extol the state in which they found themselves. That extraordinary neediness, that specific frustration of those to whom the revelation comes—that is a very real sign throughout the entire Judaeo-Christian history. It is the sign of paradox which marks the divine encounter.

On the other hand, since Nietzsche, this very fact has become the psychological temptation *par excellence*. It is one very particular aspect of the 'nothing but.' If one scrutinizes the life history of any saint or of any mystic carefully enough, one will always find the psychological reason why the supernatural happened when it happened. When God comes into our life, He 'comes in handy.' To those who think exclusively in psychological terms, this makes the supernatural experience suspect. At the same time it explains the initial caution of the Church when she is confronted with such phenomena as the apparitions of little Bernadette. In the last analysis, there is only one perfectly reliable criterion. It is, by their fruits you shall know them.

*          *          *

There are an infinite number of points at which neurosis touches upon the metaphysical. Anyone engaged in psycho-analytical work comes up against ultimate questions all the time. He may get engaged in a battle, like Freud himself. He may, like Jung, find himself involved in a sort of Gnostic experiment. He may, like Adler, run into the problem of social consciousness and social conscience. Or he may see himself forced to introduce so-called 'cultural values' into the original dynamic model, as various dissident psycho-analytic groups do. In dealing with neurosis, one always encounters something which lies beyond the purely psychological order. It just cannot be avoided: the human psyche is a metaphysical meeting-place.

Jung was originally a follower of Freud. He belonged to a small group of psychiatrists in Zurich, led by Eugen Bleuler, who accepted psycho-analysis within the framework of the traditional, academic psychiatry of the medical schools. This was not only a revolutionary step; in German-speaking countries, it was unique. Even today the psychiatric departments of nearly all German medical schools keep more or less aloof from psycho-analysis. Jung and Freud can be seen together in an early group photograph of the participants at a psycho-analytic convention in Weimar. Soon, however, Jung came to conclusions which varied from classical psycho-analysis so much that a break became inevitable.

In the original Freudian concept, the unconscious contained nothing but repressed material. According to a famous comparison, the Freudian concept of the unconscious resembles an attic into which all those things are stored which cannot be retained elsewhere in the house. The only difference is that what is repressed does not behave like old wicker chairs, bundled letters, or tailors' dummies;

it is alive. It makes a noise which often disturbs life in the living-room, or it even puts in an appearance at an inconvenient moment. In the course of his work with patients, Jung came to the conclusion that the unconscious contained not only discarded material. It seemed also to contain positive elements which could not be explained on the basis of a mechanism of disposal. Apart from the function of repression, the unconscious seemed to represent a creative principle.

Jung's point of departure was his observation that his patients produced some dream images, daytime fantasies, paintings and verbal utterances which could not be explained on the 'discard' principle and which, moreover, bore an extraordinary resemblance to the imagery and symbols of the great religions and of ancient myths and folklore. From this he concluded that we have not only an individual unconscious (which is probably nothing but the lively attic) but also a *collective unconscious*, a deep vault in which ancient images are stored, images which we have inherited from the human race. Jung called those images 'archetypes.' It is well known that this was just his starting-point and from it Jung evolved his own school of analytical psychology.

It is obvious that the religious element plays a great role in the Jungian type of analysis. It is also obvious that this school opens up fascinating problems for a Christian philosopher. There exist two separate sets of controversy. One involves a confrontation of the concepts of Jung with those of Freud. The other involves a confrontation of Jung with Catholic philosophy. Strange as it may first appear, these two controversies are related to one another and cannot be treated separately.

This can be illustrated by an example. About nine years ago I treated a patient who had been referred to me for psycho-neurotic depression. She was an unmarried woman of twenty-eight, a member of the Communist Party employed by a Communist paper. She knew nothing whatever of my own convictions, or she would probably never have come to see me in the first place. After about thirty sessions, she mentioned religion. She had come from a middle-class background, and had been brought up as a Presbyterian, but during adolescence had begun to identify herself more and more with the under-privileged and the poor and to study Karl Marx. As with so many ardent young Communists who originate in that particular layer of society, she had a good deal of unconscious religious motivation, apart from personal difficulties which had opened the way of dissent to her. She left her family, joined the Party and, out of misled idealism, lived a life of hardship and deprivation.

During that particular session, when she came to talk about matters of faith, she used an argument which one frequently encounters in atheists. Of all anti-religious arguments it is the most tragic one, and the most difficult to refute. Dostoievsky has presented it in the immortal passage of *The Brothers Karamazov* in which Ivan speaks to Alyosha. The patient spoke of the brutalities and unjust sufferings of this world (this was during the war), particularly the sufferings of children. She said that all this was quite incompatible with the idea of an all-loving, all-knowing Father in Heaven. At one point she said: 'Even if there were a God, a God who permits such things to happen—I'd rather have nothing to do with him. No, thanks. I'd rather get on without him.' With this she had a remarkably strong reaction; she cried bitterly. Obviously this was not the proper kind of atheism for a Marxist; she was too much involved for that.

At the next session, she started by relating the following dream: '*It is night. I'm walking along a dreary country road, quite alone. A drizzle of rain and snow is coming down. It is cold and dark. Suddenly a sleigh comes up behind me. It stops. On the coach seat is an old man. Inside the sleigh is a young man. They offer me a lift. I decline by saying that I'd rather walk alone. The sleigh moves on.*' She immediately associated this with the preceding session. She said it reminded her of what she had said about God. 'Here I am, alone in a dark and cold world. God stops to offer me a lift. But I decline, and prefer to walk on alone.' With this she cried again. One does not need to know Jung's theories to become aware of the religious nature of this dream. Man walking alone in the cold darkness—and spitefully refusing an offered lift! What a story for a modern Christian existentialist. There is something almost Biblical in it, with the simplicity of a parable which lifts it out of an individual setting into a region of universal validity. Which one of us can rightly say that he himself is not, at least in potentiality, the subject of the dream. It is the drama of modern man. The trinitarian element (Old Man, Young Man, Vehicle) makes it even more 'archetypical' in the Jungian sense. I later discussed this and similar productions of other patients with analysts of the Jungian school, and they told me that life constellations and images such as that are quite common in their experience. To them there was no doubt about the 'archetypical' interpretation.

In this girl's neurosis, however, the figure of the father and the figure of the brother played such a role as to allow an entirely different interpretation. Her relationship with the father and the brother, and the nature of her transference to the physician at that particular point of the analysis, were such that her 'refusal of the lift' had another meaning besides the one of which she became aware. Her spontaneous thought associations which touched upon her relationship with God made the interpretation valid on a certain plane. But the individual interpretation which refers to her early story is equally valid. Dreams and other manifestations of the unconscious can have several meanings, all of which are true. This was recognized quite early by Freud himself. He spoke of over-determination. For example, a man who dreams that he is scolded by his boss at work may be referring to his actual working situation (the so-called manifest dream content) and at the same time to a forgotten childhood scene between the father and himself. Here, however, we are referring to something more specific—namely, the co-existence of the 'archetypical' and the 'individual' plane of symbolic condensation.

The idea of two such planes of reality, superimposed one on the other, is quite familiar in the history of Christian thought. When Peter and John rushed together to the empty tomb after the resurrection, John arrived earlier but he hesitated, and Peter went in before him. John went in after Peter, saw and believed. The Fathers of the Church say that this story has, apart from its immediate significance, another meaning. The two apostles represent, as 'types,' the story of the salvation of the Jews and the Gentiles. Taking it in this sense the story also has a prophetic meaning just as, in the story of Abraham and Isaac, Abraham prefigured the Divine Father. When Christ said on the cross to Saint John the Apostle: 'Behold your Mother,' He meant not only Saint John but He addressed all mankind. Patristic literature contains many similar examples; the episode is a symbol, and the concrete historical event is the condensation of something transhistorical, and both are equally true.

There is something analogous in Jung's psychology. The dream of our patient has two meanings: one meaning is historical. It refers to a unique, one-time setting in the patient's life, namely her relation to her father and brother. Then, transposed on to another plane, the religious symbol appears. That symbol, from the point of view of the patient's life, is transhistorical. In the actual therapeutic situation the patient is perhaps never helped unless he 'works' his conflict 'through' on the personal, historical, 'Freudian' level. In most cases, perhaps in all, the patient has to live his problems, as it were. He has to experience it in the flesh, in the concrete analytical situation. Even if Freud had believed in the reality of all things of the spirit, he would probably have opposed Jung, simply on a clinical empirical basis. Jung himself compared the analytical procedure with death and rebirth. In order for this to be possible, it is necessary for the patient to journey once more through the embryonic night.

We have pointed out that the success of psycho-analysis consists in widening the gap between two worlds. One world is that of infantile fantasy and of everything with which our infantile Ego endows the objects of reality at every second of our existence. The other world is that of the adult Ego, that part of us which alone is capable of experiencing the reality of everyday life without distortion. In order to strengthen the adult Ego, the patient has to be led up against the actors and scenes of the primitive stage setting. This is tedious and painful, and it is done only by repeated experiences. The process of healing is similar to that of immunization by repeated small infections. Yet the Jungian discovery was tremendously significant. The fact that the young woman of our story experienced a spiritual crisis at that moment of the analysis was no accident.

Perhaps we are all on a dark and cold road and at one time God offers us a lift. The fact that the Jungian 'archetype' and the Freudian 'nest figure' not only do not exclude one another but are even complementary is no coincidence. It is linked up with the mystery of the Incarnation. God is our father and Christ is our brother. God Himself has acted with us on two levels. Throughout the drama of salvation—up to the Incarnation, the Sacrifice, and the Resurrection —He was a definite historical person. He was part of 'once upon a time,' but He is also universal and timeless. Whatever was 'once upon a time' also belongs to the future. 'Time future contained in time past.' Just because we are human; because our primeval experiences, all those things which determine us, are things of the flesh; because the figures which shape our fate are Father, Mother, Brother, Sister—because of all this God took human flesh. Between Jung's 'archetype' and Freud's 'nest figure' there exists not only a psychological connection but a mysterious ontological correspondence. On this basis, we now understand more fully why Freud, who denied the reality of the Spirit, came to the conclusion that God was nothing but a father figure and reconstructed 'the Christian myth' as a neurosis.

Some Freudian critics of Jung's work argue that the 'archetypes' cannot possibly have an importance in the origin of neuroses because they represent material we have learned rather than rock-bottom primitive experience. Our patient, for example, has learned about God or the Holy Trinity by a late (as neurotic patterns go) process of intellectual knowledge, in her Bible class, in Sunday school, and so on. Therefore the archetypes belong to a superficial layer of consciousness and cannot have a strong affective charge. If one denies this and assumes that the archetypes are anchored even more deeply than our individual experience in life (as is implied in some of Jung's statements), one would have to assume a sort of Platonic foreknowledge of things of the spirit—learning in Sunday school things which we have already known in a previous existence.

However, the ontological correspondence between the Freudian 'nest figure' and the Jungian archetype makes this whole argument irrelevant. Another patient who had received a little conventional religious instruction as a child, but lived all his later life in an entirely irreligious atmosphere produced the following dream during analysis: '*I am naked in a garden. Suddenly a huge man appears. I become frightened and hide behind some bushes.*' The patient associated some thoughts with this image but not the story which would immediately come into most people's minds. I finally asked him whether this reminded him of anything he'd ever heard. He seemed to rake his brain but could not think of anything. When I finally mentioned the story of Adam, he recognized it immediately and was surprised that he hadn't thought of it before. It would be sterile and formalistic to start an argument as to whether the imagery was borrowed from learned (but forgotten) material, or whether there is such a thing as archetypical stories which already exist in us when we 'learn' them. In the Judaeo-Christian order of things, the scene of shame while facing the Father is part of man's eternal story and it is not learned accidentally, whether at Sunday school or in some other way.

Many people wonder how Jung's theory can be reconciled with Christianity, since there are many archetypes, and only some of them are Christian in the way in which our patient's archetype was. In Jung's papers the primeval images of the great religions of the East often seem to play

a greater role than those of the Hebrew-Christian religion.
So do American-Indian, or Germanic, or other types.
Indeed, in Jung's writings and in those of his school one
frequently finds the atmosphere of the Museum of Comparative Religion, an air of detachment and condescension,
which deprives matters of the spirit of their devouring fire.
By studying 'religions' on the same plane as psychology, the
Jungian analyst is apt to acquire the benevolent neutrality
which characterizes many of our sociology professors. As a
German philosopher friend of mine once remarked with a
pun: '*Das gleich Gültige wird gleichgültig*' (that which is
equally relevant becomes irrelevant). The curtain of the
temple is conjured away with an elegant flourish. The border
between Nature and Grace exists no longer, and no longer
are you mortally engaged. Matters of the spirit are part
of a non-committal therapeutic method; Jacob no longer
wrestles with the Angel in a horrible grip which leaves him
for ever limping—instead he takes his daily hour of
gymnastics.

The Jungian school frequently fell in with neo-Gnostic
movements which were fashionable in the Europe between
the two wars, and which were profoundly dissociated from
the spirit of Christianity. It is probably all this which kept
Catholic scholars away from the Jungian movement for a
long time. One should have thought that the idea of the
Holy Ghost not stopping at the border of consciousness
would appeal to Catholics but, until very recently,[1] it did
not. The reality of non-Christian archetypes does not need
to have a neutralizing and killing effect. When Saint Paul
speaks of 'God who, at sundry times and in divers manners,
spoke in times past to the fathers by the prophets,' many

[1] Compare the analysis of Jung's psychology by his most outstanding
disciple among Catholic scholars, *God and the Unconscious*, by Fr Victor
White, O.P.

hold that he does not refer to the Hebrew tradition alone. The prefiguration of the Incarnation can be traced in all people; in the Hebrew people it can be traced in a very special way.

It seems to me (and this has hitherto not been studied enough) that the significance of Jung's archetypes lies in the fact that, in the history of the patient's neurosis, they *point forward*. To explain this on the basis of our example of the young Communist woman: the 'Freudian' constellation (the girl's father and brother) is that which *has happened;* the Divine Father and Son is that which, speaking in terms of the soul's movement, *will be*, that which is preparing itself in her. We shall presently come back to this. The trouble with most of the Jungian studies is the impression they convey that Grace did not come in at all; as if the Freudian structure had only been enlarged by simply adding one floor: that of the 'collective unconscious.'

# XI

# Psychiatry and the Life of the Spirit: II

He who is starving to death must be fed before he is taught;
likewise it is better for the needy 'to obtain possessions than
to pursue philosophy' (Aristotle) though the latter be of
greater worth.

ST THOMAS AQUINAS, *Summ. Theol.* II, IIae, qu.32, a.3

But as I rav'd and grew more fierce and wild
At every word,
Methought I heard one calling 'Child'
And I replied 'My Lord.'

GEORGE HERBERT

Now we come to the general question of the role of religion in psychotherapy. Many people say, if there were more faith in the world we would not have to cope with so much neurosis. This may be true as far as the role of religion in the total fabric of society is concerned. Even so it is a statement of doubtful validity. In past times when the Church dominated the life of society, there existed neurotic upheavals albeit with a different clinical appearance. One had only to remember the hysterical disturbances which, in the Middle Ages, took often the form of widespread epidemics. These disturbances have disappeared and others have come instead. It is quite possible that the mentally suffering, like the poor, will always be with us. Even if overt anxiety has increased tremendously in our time, as it seems to have, it is dangerously fallacious to link this up with the position of the person within the order of Grace. What do we know about the true spiritual state of any soul? One can show many atheists who have never known a sleepless night or a dark hour, as against saintly people of the most intense mystic life who are torn by the temptation of despair. If a person suffers from a phobia, one often hears this remark: 'If he would only pull himself together!' Many religious books on psychiatry, Catholic and non-Catholic alike, and written by well-meaning people, are on the same level. They say instead: 'If he would only have faith!' The fallacy is the same. It treats the neurosis apart from the category of suffering.

On the deepest, ontological level, it is true that where there is Neurosis there is something wrong with Faith, Hope, and Charity. If the Redemption had its full concrete impact now, in Time, there would be no anxiety. But then there would be no cancer, or tuberculosis, or head colds either. It is true that Christ said to his disciples when they were afraid: 'Oh ye of little faith.' But He Himself knew the agony of the darkest night.

Apart from the fallacy of the pat formula and the easy spiritual recipe, there is another fallacy. It is more hidden. When we say about the neurotic sufferer: 'If he only had more faith . . .' we ourselves fall into the danger of Pharisaism. We are tempted to say, or we feel without quite realizing it: 'Look at me, I believe and I have no anxiety. I thank you, God, that you have not made me like those.'

None of this is said to minimize the healing power of faith. Faith is one thing; the religious argument is another. The religious argument as a therapeutic measure stands refuted by Job, a man writhing in the grip of melancholia. After his friends have been going at him in repeated sessions, he bursts forth: 'How long do you afflict my soul, and break me in pieces with words? Behold, these ten times you confounded me, and are not ashamed to oppress me. For if I have been ignorant, my ignorance shall be with me' (Job xix, 2–4). Job was healed by faith, not by his friends' discourses.

During psycho-therapy, particularly during psycho-analysis, it is very tempting to take the 'religious line,' like Job's friends. For example, when our Communist girl had her tearful crisis, it seemed the obvious thing to pitch right in. Her relationship to me was such that I could easily have used persuasion. This was even more tempting after she had produced the dream which she herself realized was related to God. This is the moment when the physician has to resist the temptation to be a preacher. After all, she herself had supplied the interpretation, and clinical experience shows that this is much more potent than any direction on the psycho-therapist's part. In such a case there is danger that the patient might exploit the religious plane in order to escape the conflict on the natural plane. Philosophical discussions are at times used as a tool of resistance; philosophy is employed to camouflage something else. In the psycho-analytic process the *præter-verbal* (all that which lies outside the territory of the spoken word) is as important as that which is spoken. The total moral attitude of the physician, though never formulated, forms the rock bottom. Just as in a piece of music the rests are as important as the tones, the unspoken is as important in the psycho-therapeutic process as the spoken. *'Ce sont les silences qui comptent,'* a French psycho-analyst once remarked. This is the reason why a psycho-therapeutic procedure, no matter of what school, is one thing when conducted in a hedonistic *laissez-faire* atmosphere, and quite another when conducted in the atmosphere of the Gospel—though neither philosophy may ever be a point on the agenda.

In this connection we once more touch upon the question of moral judgment, which has already been dealt with in the chapter on guilt. It is a time-honoured tradition in the history of medicine that the physician is not to judge his patient morally. This principle can be followed from antiquity right through the Christian era. Apparently, in all civilizations, it is one of the unwritten rights of patients to be treated without moral judgment. Even during the puritanical Victorian period, when moral condemnation and a sort of Pharisaical discrimination belonged much more to the overt mechanics of society than now, the same unwritten law prevailed. A patient who had acquired a venereal infection extramaritally, or a young girl who had committed an abortion, had the right to be treated like any other medical case, in an atmosphere of moral detachment —regardless of the physician's personal philosophy. In the psychiatrist's case this point assumes special significance, but the situation is fundamentally the same. The psychiatrist works continuously in that peculiar twilight in which it is impossible to distinguish between freedom and necessity, and it is his work to widen the area of freedom. But he must give the sick person the benefit of the doubt. Neurotic patients are extremely sensitive to this. They 'feel' it if there is even a trace of condemnation, though never formulated, in the very depth of the physician's mind. And, once that exists, the therapeutic relationship is destroyed. Nowhere does the saving power of charity become more apparent.

It often happens, for example, that the patient, out of motives which are related to certain phases of transference, wants to 'arouse' the physician of whose Christian convictions he is aware. Or he wants, unconsciously, to be condemned. This is not a healthy desire for moral restitution but a wish to re-enact, on the therapeutic stage, an infantile scene. This happens particularly in patients with a-social or anti-social behaviour. A thirty-four-year-old married woman, the mother of two boys (one eight, the other six) was referred to me because of a serious character neurosis which manifested itself in drinking, promiscuity, and various forms of social scandal which were at times quite startling. She had been brought up as a Catholic but had ceased practising her religion many years before. Like many character neuroses of that particular a-social pattern, her state bordered on the psychotic. On one occasion she told the story of having had sexual relations with a man, not her husband, in front of her two boys. There is no doubt whatsoever that I should have lost her if I had begun to 'preach,' or appeal to her sense of rectitude, or do anything along those lines. At times it was apparent that she related her stories (which were true) in the most scandalizing terms because she wanted a (moral) beating. The fact that her desire for punishment, rejection, or condemnation within the psycho-therapeutic situation was frustrated contributed powerfully to her moral regeneration. This sounds paradoxical. There is no contradiction between this and what has been remarked in the preceding paragraph. On the contrary. Whether the physician maintains an attitude of 'Judge not!' out of supernatural motives, or whether he maintains a neutral attitude because he thinks that morality is a pragmatic but arbitrary social fiction—these are two opposite worlds from the point of view of the inner dynamics of treatment, particularly the dynamics of transference. When I am confronted with a case of anti-social or a-social tendencies, no matter how scandalizing to my sense of moral harmony, my psycho-analytic knowledge of myself teaches me that, but for a trivial change of circumstances, I might be in the patient's shoes and doing the things he is doing. This is where psycho-analysis has deepened and enriched the Christian moral conscience. On the other hand, this is precisely the point at which the Christian moral conscience is able to deepen and enrich psycho-analysis.

In this connection we have to refer briefly once more to Jung. In cases like that of the promiscuous woman, one can observe that during the therapeutic process fantasies and images turn up which seem to be related to Jungian archetypes. This is at times the first indication of a creative solution of the neurotic conflict. Frequently one is able to explain the choice of symbols merely on the basis of the mechanism of transference, and out of the fact that the patient is approaching the road towards sublimation. This is obvious whenever the symbols are not religious.

I worked at one time in an out-patient department with a juvenile delinquent. This boy, whom I saw first when he was sixteen, had a long record of seriously anti-social activities, with trials in Juvenile Courts and several periods in reformatories. He was a pleasant, very intelligent lad who had, among other things, lacked any healthy kind of identification with the father. He had not been able to cope with unconscious homosexual trends, and behind his destructiveness was a terrible fear of weakness and passivity. His relationship with me was very stormy. A lot of the things he did and said were based on mechanisms quite similar to that of the patient quoted above. On one occasion he reported the following dream: *'The violinist Isaac Stern is playing the Mendelssohn violin concerto. I am standing behind him with a half-size violin, and we both play the*

*concerto* unisono, *stroke for stroke*.' The patient knew that
I was interested in music; so was he. He actually played
the 'cello, at that time, as a beginner. Even for someone not
acquainted with the Freudian method of interpretation, the
identity of the concert violinist with the doctor must be
obvious from the identity of names. Without touching upon
all the implications of this dream, the state of his relationship to me at that time is also obvious. His strong craving
for identification is beautifully symbolized. Now the choice
of symbol is no coincidence. The fact that the relationship
is 'non-carnal' to that extent, that it expresses itself in
music and in musical instruments, is not only due to an
unconscious 'censor,' a 'beautifier' as it were—the unconscious already indicates the road towards sublimation.
(This boy is today a successful science student, and has
not had any relapses into his anti-social activities, though
he still has far to go.)

The point I wanted to make is that the dream chooses
symbolic material which is explained out of certain features
of the transference, and which indicates *things to be*. If a
patient in a similar situation has dreams with religious
images, the reason for such a choice of symbols might be
similar. This, for example, could be observed in the case
of the promiscuous woman. In other words, the coincidence
of religious symbols is dynamically significant (from the
point of view of 'sublimation' and 'transference') but it
does not make the assumption of true archetypes necessary.

This may sound as if we were trying to say that that
which is of the spiritual order were one thing and the sickness another; or that the life of prayer and of the sacraments
play no role when it comes to mental suffering. This would
be a wrong impression. My purpose is to warn against a
false 'spirituality' in the approach to neurotic suffering;

to show that often the vessel of reception is sick so that which is of the supernatural order is incapable of penetrating in a way we are used to when we think of the spiritual life; to show how subtle and complex the relationship between Grace and Nature is in those cases in which the vessel is disfigured; to emphasize how the structure of the neurotic illness is intimately interwoven with profound biological layers of the personality.

This does not mean that the life of prayer loses its significance in that area. Wherever there is enough faith left, it works in its own mysterious way. I do not like to talk about the work of Alcoholics Anonymous in terms of 'sublimation,' because it is too mechanistic an explanation. Mat Talbot was cured of alcoholism much more effectively than any form of psycho-therapy could ever have achieved it. But this is in the nature of *gratia gratis data*. The same thing can probably be said of many persons who achieved sanctity out of a background of neurosis. Ever since the time of the Psalmist, man has turned to God whenever he was beset by worries and conflicts. From the time of the Fathers of the Church until now, many beautiful spiritual treatises have been written especially designed for those who labour and mourn. Catholic literature is probably the richest in the world precisely for that purpose. All this is outside the range of the present study. What we want to discuss here are those huge dark uncharted areas in which the needle of the spiritual compass itself seems to deviate.

There are phases during which the spiritual life of a person takes on a strange colouring; phases which are marked by turmoil and upheaval; phases during which the metaphysical chasm opens up, and the person is threatened by primeval fear or swallowed up in ecstasy. This happens particularly during the turning points of life, during adolescence and during the climacteric phase. It is here where the distinction between mystical experience and clinical phenomenon, between compulsiveness and asceticism, between elements of the 'nothing but' and elements of a transcendental order, is often most difficult. Here a physician of religious convictions particularly needs careful discernment, a respect for the mystery of the person, and just plain clinical experience.

At times it is practically necessary to illuminate that strange frontier area in which Neurosis and Faith meet. In these instances the physician himself, no matter how firm his belief is, has to use the reductive method, the argument of 'nothing but.' By and large the distinction between morbid and healthy is not difficult. For example, where spiritual asceticism ends and compulsiveness (the 'scruple') begins is usually quite apparent in the picture of the total personality. What we have said about sanctity holds true also here: quite often, the distinction between what is healthy and what is morbid in the spiritual life comes down to the simple rule—by their fruits you shall know them.

We have seen that, in distinguishing the healthy from the morbid, it is not the phenomenological structure which matters. If the creative artist or the mystic hears something which for us 'is not there,' he is outside the range of the normal, but he may be supra-normal rather than abnormal. What matters is the content and above all, to use the words of the gospel, the 'fruits.'

In a rationalist society, *all* faith is abnormal. We are fools in Christ. To feel certainty about something we have not seen, and which in its manifestations runs against the ordinary laws of Nature, is madness as long as experimental evidence is the sole criterion of truth. Phenomenologically there is a close resemblance between faith and paranoia. Yet in content they are perfectly opposed to each other. Paranoia, according to classical descriptive psychiatry (and in this connection I am not going into the psycho-analytical interpretation), is characterized by delusional ideas which form a logically coherent system of thought and leave the rest of the personality intact. A paranoiac may have an extraordinary set of ideas about the role of, let us say, the Freemasons in his life and in the world in general. You may meet him in a railway compartment, have a couple of hours of pleasant conversation, and never realize that he is a madman unless you or he happen to touch on his subject. Even then, if he is intelligent and a good talker, you may have the feeling after listening for a while: 'Maybe he's got something there.' Paranoiac patients have been known to influence juries in court. It is, incidentally, no coincidence that I chose the example of Freemasons. All paranoiac patients (the condition in its pure clinical form is rare), no matter whether we encounter them in mental hospitals in Paris, New York, or Rio, have certain pet themes, particularly the Jews, the Freemasons, the Communists, and the Catholic Church. To the ordinary man these groups have an air of ubiquitousness and mysteriousness, and a paranoiac patient sees hints in the common occurrences of everyday life. He sees 'things behind things' where we do not see them. This is the most characteristic feature in the phenomenology of paranoia. The German General Ludendorff (who was convinced there was an extremely involved world conspiracy which included Jews, Freemasons, the Vatican, and the Kremlin) discovered, intricately disguised, the sign of the Freemasons in the ornamented margin of the printed invitation to a banquet given in his honour; he immediately cancelled his acceptance.

The close phenomenological relationship of paranoia and faith is evident. Faith and paranoia are more akin to each other than they are to the world of scientific certitude. We, the faithful, hold a basic truth which is foolish in the eyes of the world, and out of which a logically coherent system of thought develops. We, too, see 'things behind things.' To us, too, the seemingly haphazard occurrences of everyday life reveal a mysterious pattern. But while the climate of paranoia is distrust and its fruit is hatred, the climate of faith is confidence and its fruit is love. Paranoia is the mirror image of faith in an ugly distortion. Just as the saint has no difficulty in recognizing other persons as ambassadors of Christ, the paranoiac patient easily sees other people as ambassadors of the hated adversary. This is most significant for the psychology of masses; in times of political restlessness, paranoiac personalities (blatant clinical and milder subclinical cases) come to the front. They have an extraordinary power to mobilize latent paranoid tendencies in the population. Vigilance turns into distrust. And in the end hatred becomes a strange bond of union. In totalitarian countries that strange Gift of Distrust, the readiness to see machinations behind events, is systematically mobilized and channelled.

There is another difference between paranoia and faith. The paranoiac patient has no choice between doubt and certainty. In the classical definition, paranoiac delusions are held with absolute certainty and cannot be shaken. Yet it is the characteristic feature of faith that it can be tried. The person who has faith is aware of the fact that there exists no scientific proof. Faith is blind. There are mystics who hold that even the Blessed Virgin lived on faith up to the hour of the Resurrection. She was tried. Thus faith is inextricably interwoven with Love and Hope, not only as regards the *content* of what we believe but also as regards the nature of the *inner movement*.

To the spiritual life of most Catholic people, the Gospel of Rationalism and Pragmatism constitutes no danger. It constitutes a danger in so far as it forms part of the fabric of the society in which they live but it is not much of an interior danger. To many of us the true danger lies somewhere else. It is more subtle but no less formidable. It is characterized by what one might perhaps best call the 'communion of distrust.' Today, while we are facing the evil of Communism, vigilance is more necessary than at any other time. Everybody agrees about that. But vigilance has a tendency to open, in a subtle and imperceptible way, frontiers in the human soul which had better be for ever closed. Vigilance in the face of evil may give rise to preoccupation with evil. And, as the Fathers of the Church taught, if we are unduly preoccupied by evil, we become evil. There is danger in giving more thought to the things we are *against* than the things we are *for*. It is easier to have distrust than to have faith. The story of the early church shows clearly that it is the *positive* in faith which conquers the world.

An interesting story from the life of Saint Thérèse of Lisieux concerns a book written by a convert, presenting what today would be called the 'inside story' of the Freemasons. This book was apparently a best-seller at that time and it was enthusiastically received by the good nuns of her community. Only Thérèse, in opposition to her superior and everybody else, disliked it intensely. The author was later unmasked as a psychopathic swindler. Today, when Communists and secret Communist machinations present an objective danger, we face a great pitfall.

It is not a question of paranoia in the clinical sense. It is an imponderable something which happens to a Community of Faith. We have our nose to the ground to ferret out the scent of the adversary; we have our ears to the ground to hear the distant rumbling; before we know it, something decisive has happened to us. We are no longer upright. Our gaze is no longer fixed on God and Man in charity.

As it is at times important to scrutinize spiritual upheavals purely on the psychological plane, it is equally important to scrutinize crises of doubt and unbelief in the same way. Lack of faith or loss of faith is at times so obviously structured within the entire context of the neurosis that anyone but the most prejudiced must see the connection. In the numberless psycho-analytical papers on religious phenomena, studies which usually end up by reducing everything spiritual to the dynamic formula, hardly anything has ever been said about *the neurosis of unbelief*. This is not surprising, since to most investigators faith ('the certainty of things we have not seen') is an abnormal or at least a suspect phenomenon.

In my own experience, lack of religious faith or loss of faith has often proved to be a serious indication of a disordered person. The most frequent mechanism I have encountered can perhaps best be described as follows. In order to have faith, we have to be childlike. Now in terms of our unconscious—that is to say, in the Freudian archaic strata which make up the preconceptual and instinctual— that which is childlike is pregenital. The believer is in a state of passive receptiveness. If we refuse to believe something, we say: 'You can't make me swallow that.' Of a person who believes something readily or without difficulty, we say: 'He swallowed it hook, line, and sinker.' A person who believes too easily is called 'gullible' or a 'sucker.' In German one says about a lifelong belief: 'He took it in with his mother's milk.' In the life of the unconscious, on the purely natural plane believing is an oral mechanism.

I have seen many cases in which this is quite apparent. In a great number of neurotic people, the dynamic constellation of childhood is such that childlikeness means powerlessness. In their fantasy that which is pregenital is emasculated. If you are passive-receptive, if you 'swallow' things, all your power and your potential aggressiveness disappear. This is a bizarre and fearful fantasy. In everyday language, not only are you made to 'swallow' beliefs, you are also 'taken in.' I have also noticed that neurotic unbelievers in their fantasies endow the purely intellectual, non-intuitive and non-poetic side of human thought (the sort of thinking which a logical positivist would claim to be the only proper mode of human reason) with extraordinary, limitless power.

I once treated a man in his early forties, a very successful business man, who had symptoms of anxiety and a problem of overt marital maladjustment. This man came from a very religious Protestant background. He had known poverty in his childhood, but had become wealthy himself. The father had been a poor man, according to the patient, weak and passive. The mother had apparently been quite compulsive, particularly when it came to religious practices. There were three brothers and four sisters; the parents had shown considerable favouritism towards an older brother. (I cannot go into all the ramifications of the story, important though they are for the understanding of his case, but I shall tell only what is relevant to the present argument.) Early in life our patient had discarded his religious faith.

He said it was 'all boloney.' In the beginning of our
relationship he told me that his despising of religion might
be due to the fact that he associated it with the 'smallness'
of his parents' life, the poverty of his childhood and so on.
This feeling was not without ambivalence. On one occasion
he told me that he still felt suddenly and strangely affected
whenever he heard a hymn or a Bible story. On the whole,
however, his outlook was belligerently rationalistic. His
only faith was a belief in technical progress, and in all the
things which were 'smart' and 'modern.' Although very
rich, he was a great admirer of Stalin, whom he saw, in
terms of international politics, as a 'strong rebel.' He himself
had an insatiable need for material security, and in material
success and cleverness he had outdone all his brothers.
During the analytical process, he produced fantasies which
showed that he was simply terrified by his own potential
femininity, by all that was passive-receptive. There were
reasons for this which I shall not discuss here in detail.
Suffice it to say that behind his rejection of religion there
was that same fear of the passive-receptive. To be passive
and receptive was to him a fantasy of utter annihilation.
(On one occasion this patient told of an anxiety dream in
which he was a piece of blotting-paper absorbing milk. In
this image, he was a 'sucker' *par excellence*.)

When it comes to the neurosis of unbelief, this pattern
is typical and repetitive. One could say that to this man
faith was associated with the oppressive atmosphere of
poverty or of narrowness, and leave it at that. In our
psycho-analytical experience this would not be enough. You
have to go down to the archaic level of the 'somatic cosmos,'
the 'Freudian' level, really to understand this neurosis.

The searching reason of science is a masculine, aggressive principle. It pierces the reality of objects. It proceeds

according to a plan of attack. The world of faith is just the opposite. 'I shall comfort you as a mother comforts.' 'Unless you be like unto one of these children . . .' We have to remain open for God. We have to wait for Him. Mankind's relationship to God contains the relationship of the bride to the groom; according to the Gospel, we are seed grounds. There is also a relationship of child to mother. Just as science is a masculine principle, wisdom (*Sophia*) is in classic imagery and in the life of the unconscious a feminine principle. She receives and she nourishes, like nature itself.

A man who denies these elements in himself is deeply affected. He is denatured. So often in our work people tell us how, during adolescence, they had an experience of awakening, something like a conversion—but away from faith. From then on truth was limited only to that which callipers and test-tubes taught. Here, more than anywhere else, the neurosis of Western man and the individual neurosis overlap. Unless Reason and Contemplation are balanced, we are sick. Reason tackles problems; it is associated with activity. Contemplation beholds mysteries; it is associated with silence. Scripture tells us how the prophet Ezekiel was made to swallow a scroll. The modern sceptic refuses to swallow anything. He does not want to take in for fear of being taken in.

It is interesting how anxiety manifests itself on the natural level. In the mass of population as a whole it would seem that 'oral' insatiability is steadily on the increase. From the increase of alcoholism down to the harmless levels of oral pleasures (which have created entire industries), anxiety appears to assume a uniform epidemic pattern. Psycho-analytically there exists a close relationship between oral and visual primitive libidinal patterns, which means that the tremendous modern appeal of moving pictures, television, and illustrated magazines must be included in the pattern. This is almost like an inversion of the Christian ideal of contemplation in which the primitive instinctual forces are harnessed and the person keeps himself 'open' for the word of God.

Thus, with many of us, the restless, searching, analytical power of the intellect which pries open the secrets of Matter has become the only aspect of Truth. We are no longer able to sit still, to wait, to listen. We refuse to be receptive. We have to create a continuous noise to drown out the stillness of the Word. This disequilibrium in our mind's fundamental duality, this strange form of maleness (in the widest sense of the psycho-analytic meaning) refers not only to the neurosis of the single individuals whose cases I have just mentioned. It has become for all of us an existential question. We understand why Goethe, who was so wary of the dangers of modern rationalism, had his extraordinary mystic insight into the 'Eternal-Feminine which guides us on.' We understand why Soloviev, only a short time before the Russian catastrophe, had his vision of *Sophia*. Above all, we understand why the Blessed Virgin has played such an eminent role in the life of the Church during the last century and this.

It also explains something else. In the life of modern mystics there is a particular emphasis on simplicity, on childlikeness. In phenomenology it is characteristic that, but for an apparently trivial difference, that which is morbid may be healthy in the highest meaning of the word. The English language expresses this difference in the words 'childish' and 'childlike'; to be the first is to be silly and to be the second is wise. We have seen that all neurosis means either arrestation at, or regression to, the infantile level. Apart from that primeval schema of the child, there is another child in every one of us. That is the child we have to keep preciously alive. The world of neurosis is characterized by an infantile dependence on people, on things; the world of faith is characterized by a childlike dependence on God. The one must diminish so that the other can be completed.

# XII      Beyond Psychology

> But there is the Christian Church—a factor to be reckoned
> with. It may have to undergo martyrdom in the future world-
> state, but, as it compelled the Roman world-state in the end
> to make at any rate formal submission to Christ, it might
> again, by the way of martyrdom, conquer the scientific
> rationalist world-state of the future.
>
> DR EDWYN BEVAN, in a letter to Arnold Toynbee

THE preceding study is primarily a historical argument.
The entire question of psychiatry and religion has
arisen in our time because with certain psychological
discoveries the Christian concept of Man appeared to
be seriously challenged. However, in the course of this
study another aspect of the question has presented itself:
psychiatry and the social sciences are invading areas in
everyday life which, in the order of Grace, cannot remain
indifferent; this is happening at a time when man's relationship to his work and to his co-worker has become de-per-
sonalized. All this poses a very serious question to those
who look at human history from a Christocentric point of
view. If the Comtean ideal were ever really fulfilled, if the
'third revolution' were to succeed, if faith were entirely
replaced by science, then psychology and psychiatry would
play a central role. What would that role be?

Various trends in present-day psychiatry, of which
psycho-analysis is just one, have been presented in their

historical setting. However, the 'historical' approach made it necessary to look at psycho-analysis twice, as it were. First we considered it in its entirety, not only its scientific structure but the philosophical superstructure on top. Then we took a second look. The superstructure was removed and the building was investigated in its basic features, lifted out of the general positivist stream of our time.

In speaking of the psycho-analyst turned philosopher, of his debunking attitude, the glee with which he destroys man's spiritual 'illusions'—we remarked that there is nothing new in this. We said that actually all discoveries since the end of the Middle Ages have automatically, as it were, become theories of debunking. Freud has already observed this and given it a remarkable interpretation He has indicated in his frequently quoted remark on the 'insults' which mankind has received since the Renaissance. At the time when resistance to psycho-analysis was at its height he remarked that part of this resistance could be explained on the basis of a deep wound to human pride. The wound, he said, was not the first one. Until the time of Copernicus man lived in a geocentric cosmos. The earth, man's dwelling-place, was the very centre of things, and everything else turned around it. With Copernicus the earth was demoted to a mere speck somewhere in the Galaxy. What a blow to Man's pride! This was, as Freud called it, the cosmic insult. After that there was at least the illusion left that man was the king of living creatures, the centre of creation on this earth. But with Darwin and the biological evolutionists even this illusion seemed destroyed. Man as a creature was dethroned. He suddenly appeared as the sort of chance product of a seemingly blind biological process, just a loose link at the end of a chain. This was, in Freud's words, the biological insult. Now something similar happened with the advent of psycho-analysis and its discovery of the unconscious. Human Reason, royal and autonomous, became a mere surface ripple over an ocean of dark mysterious currents which seem to be guided by blind, irrational forces. This was the psychological insult. The entire resistance against psycho-analysis looked like a patient's last-ditch fight to preserve at least a remnant of narcissism (an infantile fantasy of the self).

Actually, there have been other insults. For instance, Marx's dialectical materialism works on the assumption that all of mankind's proud achievements in the cultural field, the arts and sciences, in fact the entire drama of human history, can be explained on the basis of economic data, by the tension between economic factors—to put it plainly, by the history of greed. According to the writings of Marx and Lenin, the entire spiritual history of mankind is determined by and can be explained on the basis of a rather vulgar process. This sounds primitive and seems to be an insult to our intelligence. But when one reads the classical Marxist writings it is not at all as stupid as it sounds. Given a purely material concept of man, believing, as most of us do, that there is nothing but Nature to go on, it makes more sense than a good many philosophies which are being handed out to us today. The very thought of such a concept of history makes most of us wince. Another wound! One could call this the cultural insult.

Look at what has happened to the Christian within four centuries. First he is evicted from a geocentric cosmos. Then he is told that his higher achievements are accidental by-products of the fight for food. Then he is demoted to the position of a cousin in the monkey family. And finally his reason is declared to be a precariously fragile something determined by forces the very nature of which are obscure to him.

Let us assume, as we have done in this book, that we are witnessing here something like a revolution (centred around the psychological sciences in the widest sense of the word), a revolution which may lead to similarly profound consequences—what does this mean from the Christian point of view of history? To begin with, we see that man is trying to tackle his problems on the natural plane. Nothing exists which transcends the conclusions derived from material data. However, something like a descending scale can be observed: first, it was the social and economic aspect of the human animal which promised the solution (in dialectical materialism). Then it was the biological and racial aspect (in Nazism). Finally it is the psychological aspect. However, this descending scale cannot be a coincidence: it looks almost as if a materialist philosophy of man were worming its way gradually from a place somewhere 'outside' towards the inmost core of the human person.

In the course of these revolutions, the image of man as presented to us in the Gospel has become increasingly distorted. One might argue that a materialist theory of economic justice is, comparatively speaking, more innocuous than a materialist theory of the human person. However, the effect turns out to be quite different from what was expected. The materialist, finally confronted with the psyche, comes up against something which destroys his original premises. To use Hegelian terms, materialism creates its own antithesis and finally negates itself. From this *a new synthesis* ought to arise.

As a matter of fact, it does. The first impression is quite deceptive; all we can see is the most extraordinary state of spiritual pride in which we find ourselves. In that sense, the process of 'reducing' man has not been successful. Man who thought of himself as an image of God, with a very elevated position in the Universe, gets up from the couch after four centuries of very convincing insights—further than ever removed from humility! This is the greatest paradox of all. Men used to bow when they prayed to a God who 'established the nature of man in wondrous dignity and even more wondrously renewed it.' Now that they have been diminished to points of reference shifting within an estranged universe, they seem more cocksure than ever.[1] As Pascal has pointed out, to live in a universe without Christ at its centre induces tremendous anxiety. To live as an individual with a psyche without Christ at the centre should induce even more anxiety, and I strongly suspect that our cocksureness is something like whistling in the dark.

The second impression of this revolution is altogether different. When we regard psycho-analysis in its fundamental features, freed from its nineteenth-century accretions, something startling emerges. It suddenly moves into a historical context quite opposite to the one in which we saw it first. When we look at the entire preceding study (of which psycho-analysis forms only a part) we can observe two trends. One trend in the history of modern psychiatry is characterized by the fact that psychic data are treated as *objects*—the way in which the zoologist looks at butterflies, the geologist at minerals, and the chemist at molecules. When the clinician of the nineteenth century classified 'entities' of mental diseases he treated these diseases as species, comparable to classifiable objects; when the

[1] After writing these lines, I found the same thought expressed by Gabriel Marcel in his book, *Être et Avoir*.

Pavlovian physiologist studies the behaviour of man under the aspect of interacting reflexes, he studies an object of mechanics; when the behaviourist studies the 'social reflex' by using the 'discrimination cage' and arrives at the formulation of behaviour laws, he treats social phenomena as if they were the object of a special kind of physics; when the cybernetics man speaks of mental breakdowns in terms of cell circuits, he also treats psychic phenomena like objects of physics; when the 'communications' man investigates the living together of groups of people on the basis of the 'communication model', he treats social phenomena as if they were the object of a kind of engineering; whenever the psychologist evolves a test which yields graphs and percentages, he translates, as it were, something which has once been a psychic element and studies it as if it were an object; and so on.

The second trend which we have indicated throughout this book is characterized by the absence of an object in the sense of the natural sciences. 'Absence of an object' appears paradoxical. In the relationship between psychoanalyst and patient there exists, to borrow terms which modern philosophers[1] have used in a somewhat different connection, not a relationship of *I* and *it*, or *I* and *they*—there exists only '*I* and *Thou*.' If one removes from psychoanalysis all secondary elaborations (the terminology which makes things appear mechanical and the philosophy which makes them appear determinist and materialist), then it is first and foremost the psychology of *I* and *Thou*.

The relationship of *I* and *Thou* is mysterious. In the world of the natural sciences no two objects can be in the same place at the same time. In the relationship of *I* and *Thou* there is an interpenetration of being. This is the reason

[1] Particularly Max Scheler and Gabriel Marcel.

why we dwelt at such length on empathy and connaturality. Contrary to the '*I* and *it*' or '*I* and *they*' the relationship of '*I* and *Thou*' is, on the natural plane, related to love— either positively or negatively. It cannot be neutral. Objects in mathematical space are not only separate; they are also opaque. The '*I* and *Thou*' is an illuminating insight. Here the light of reason and the light of charity belong together. The '*I* and *Thou*' contains an implicitly metaphysical quality. Now we understand much better why materialistic thinkers, either of the positivist or the Marxist variety, usually view the entire business of psycho-analysis with suspicion.

After these distinctions we are in a better position to answer the question we asked in the beginning of this chapter. Let us suppose one set out to establish a dehumanized society, a society of the beehive, something comparable to a smoothly-running machine—for one's official psychology there would be no choice. It would have to be a psychology of *I* and *it*, *I* and *they*, Pavlovian mechanic sets, cybernetics or communication models, discrimination cages, graphs and formulas, personality tests, group dynamics and so on. That is the only kind of psychology which enables us to *run* people. The psychology of *I* and *it*, or *I* and *they*, is the psychology of the manager. Descartes, one of the great inaugurators of modern scientific thought, made a distinction between the things of our inner experience (*res cognita*) and things of the world of material objects (*res extensa*). If we want to *manage* human affairs we have to treat psychic data as if they were part of some huge *res extensa*. The result is not pleasant. It does not make any difference whether you look at man as a reflex mechanism as the Soviet psychiatrists do, or as a set of chromosomes as the Nazi psychiatrists did, or from the point of view of some

Comtean sociological ideal. The outcome is always the same. It always goes strictly against the dignity of the human person.

When science replaces faith, then we are in a position of playing God. And when we play God, the things we do are usually not nice. I strongly suspect an inner connection between the Pavlovian reflex machine and the technique of obtaining confessions in the Soviet Union. If the connection is not one of method, it is certainly one of philosophy. There certainly was a connection between the chromosome sets and that ghastly Sterilization Board in Nazi Germany. I hate to think what the results of our laboratories for group dynamics might be in a managerial society.

The psychiatrist whose ideas about the communication model we have outlined said that we must get away from Aristotelian concepts. Our thinking must become 'non-Aristotelian' and 'field-theoretical.' This means, in plain language, that in order to see human society as a communication machine, man has to stop being man. Aristotle, and a few others after him, were quite wrong in assuming that human beings have eternal qualities which set them apart from all other things in the universe and remain immutable under all conditions. In other words, for the psychology of the *it* and the *they*, we have to forget about the human person as a person in the sense in which Aristotle or Saint Thomas mean it. We have to see him as an object or, at best, as an individual.[1]

Some time during the war a colleague of mine who had just returned from a meeting of psychiatrists of the Armed Forces told me quite enthusiastically, obviously without realizing what he was saying: 'They have tried out some

[1] The term 'individual' (unit) as opposed to 'person' is here used in the sense of Thomist philosophy.

interesting rapid personality tests for screening personnel. One fellow reported a test which takes exactly ten minutes.' The essence of that test was that the man to be investigated had to appear naked with his serial number written across his chest. This could easily be arranged because the subject had probably just finished his physical examination. They had experimentally established, my friend told me, that a man who is completely undressed is less apt to tell lies about himself. The psychiatrist of the examining board would furtively look up the serial number in a list. He then would address the candidate by his first name. It had been established that a man who appears naked before an examiner and is unexpectedly addressed by his first name will, during a brief conversation, reveal essential traits of his personality and things which otherwise might come out only in many hours of history-taking.

It is irrelevant that the test in that specific form has apparently never been adopted. Moreover, the story has not been told here in order to question the importance or validity of screening. There are situations in which people have to be tested before they are given certain jobs. The story is told because of its symbolic implications, as a striking example of a managerial psychology. Just try to conjure up a society in which such a rapid testing of the personality would be a *typical* scene. Think for a moment how the word 'personality' is being used here in contrast to the meaning of 'personality' in Catholic philosophy. And quite a few Catholics who are scandalized by what they know about psycho-analysis would not be at all shocked by that scene. We are all so impregnated by the Cartesian fallacy, which is the very air we breathe, that we fail to see anything wrong with it. Yet, if a poet wanted to write something like an eschatological play about our time—

what material! The naked man, with his serial number across his chest, addressed by his Christian name, having his personality assessed: it would not take much to make it look like a mock scene of Judgment.

The psycho-analytic procedure is essentially different from all this. As we have shown, this is not immediately obvious. From the beginning the poetic-intuitive nature of the method was camouflaged by the terminology. Freud had to form easily communicable concepts. Therefore he presented his findings in words which make us think of diagrams and models. Moreover, he remained, one might almost say, anxiously deterministic. Any decent scientist with laboratory training had to keep away from ideas of finality, to say nothing of the idea of ultimate finality. More-over, psycho-analysis eagerly welcomed any confirmation which came from animal experiments and brain physiology. There is nothing wrong with all this but it meant that an extraordinary body of human intuitive understanding became more and more assimilated to and embedded in a scientific world which is that of the animal and the machine.

Take all this away and there remains a core—the drama of *I* and *Thou*, the human dialogue. The Communists saw quite clearly that this is incompatible with the *I* and *they*. They are much more logical than we. The *I* and *Thou* has no place in the beehive. In the psycho-analytic situation there always remains a chink through which love and freedom may come in. It is impossible to baptize reflex man, or the cybernetics model or the communication set, whether it be composed of groups of people or groups of cells. But the method of *I* and *Thou* asks bluntly, as it were, to be Christianized.

To illustrate this let us once more go back to the story of the old immigrant which was told in the second chapter.

The psychiatrist who treated him, who recognized the hidden symbolic disguises in his symptoms, and who finally produced the old consul-general and who enacted the scenes which brought about the solution of the conflict, was personally not a believing Christian. In fact he did not believe in anything, as far as I know. He did only what he thought was scientifically correct. Yet the solution of the problem, the denouement of our story, appeared similar to a solution dictated by wisdom and charity. The story of the old consul, the scene of forgiveness, the catharsis following a seemingly inescapable nightmare of guilt and punishment, was a human solution.

Now with this we come to a remarkable paradox. If a physician had kept away from psycho-analytic teaching because it might be incompatible with Christian doctrine he might have approached our patient with all these psychiatric methods which are doctrinally 'safe.' He might have clung anxiously to concepts of classical descriptive psychiatry. In that case he might have labelled our patient with a clinical term and given him some physical form of treatment, such as electro-shock ('There is nothing wrong with it'). I have seen many examples of this. In doing so he would actually have acted in a less Christian way than the psycho-analyst who professed no religious belief. In remaining on the strictly physiological level (the electric treatment does have an effect on the cellular mechanisms of certain disorders of the affects), he would have kept a safe Cartesian double-ledger.[1] We are so often guilty of

[1] It is at times shocking to see how insensitive some Catholics (in America) have become to what one might call the technocratic heresy. I have come across departments of psychology in Catholic universities in which numerous 'personality problems' were studied with the aid of apparatuses, graphic symbols, statistics, questionnaires, tape recordings, and so on, in other words with the aid of the gadget, not only in the sense of concrete machinery but in the sense of an entire *methodological*

that. But the inner drama of our patient's life would not have been touched. Empathic knowledge is, as we saw, on the natural level akin to charity. And, as we have shown, in enlarging the frontiers of empathy we gain more and more ground for charity.

When our patient, after many years of unconsciously imposed penance, wanted to inflict on himself the capital punishment, and when (with the aid and the understanding of the psycho-analyst) that scene of reconciliation was enacted, the scene of the forgiving father—we saw, as it were, the raw material for a Christian solution. But the material remains material. There is to the faithful Christian an aspect of guilt and atonement which has not been touched. The therapy was effective. But we know that guilt and redemption have a supernatural aspect. That aspect has not been approached during the entire procedure. What the therapist has achieved at best is a primitive foreshadowing

---

*atmosphere.* Now in such an atmosphere you are bound to slide into an area in which science becomes a depersonalizing force. Instead of moving towards the human person you move away from it. The transition is often subtle and imperceptible. Before you know it the machine has got the better of you. Some years ago a priest who does a lot of marital counselling told me that he uses, I have forgotten whether for teaching or for research, the tape recorder. Something very serious has gone wrong here. It is not a question of the ethics of secrecy. Many conversations like this could be tape-recorded in such a way that personal secrecy is delicately maintained. The danger lies somewhere else. Counselling is the prototype of the human dialogue. In a sense, all human dialogue is unique and irretrievable. It is sacred whether it occurs in the sacramental setting or not. When you fix it in order to be able to 'play it back' you make a decisive step. My first contact with all this was a young priest whom I met many years ago and who told me that one of his subjects at the seminary was psychology. I asked what he had studied and he said he had so far had only a course in statistics. This means that this young man who would later be a director of souls was first initiated into the field of psychology by something which once and for all placed it in the 'strictly scientific category'—something hopelessly removed from, say, the psychology of a Saint Francis of Sales. It is hard to understand why we should be so little sensitive to that technocratic fallacy. Perhaps it springs from a human weakness to live up to the scientific Joneses. Or it may be that the objective psychology of the laboratory is a shield against anxiety.

of something which lies beyond the psychological plane.
Grace builds on Nature. From that point of view the
therapist has worked in the right direction. He has prepared the patient for something. To the Christian there is
something most essential to our patient's life which the
therapeutic process cannot solve.

Let us suppose that there were thousands of psycho-
analysts who with infinite patience and kindness, and with
an ingenious degree of empathy, were able to follow neurotic
suffering to its last ramification and led their patients up
to a final denouement similar to the one in the case of our
old immigrant. If we were then made to believe that the
mystery of guilt and suffering had been solved in these
cases we would reach a most extraordinary state of affairs.
This would actually constitute a state of the most subtle
and therefore most deadly pride. That drama which goes
on only between the soul of a man and the heart of Christ
would be conjured away. It would mean that man ends
where psychology ends. The human person would be
without that element of Above and Below. The human
dialogue would resolve all mysteries. There would be
nothing beyond it.

Thus we see that, while the psychology of *I* and *they*
is the psychology of collectivism, the pitfall of psycho-
analysis is individualism. If one gave (in some Orwellian
story) a monistic significance to the psychology of *I* and
*they*—if one evolved it into a *technique of living*, into something which expands into the vacuum left by secularism—
the psychologist would be a demiurge, a re-enactment of
God the Creator. If psycho-analysis assumed such a position, the psychologist would be a re-enactment of God the
Redeemer.

Nevertheless, the fact remains that psycho-analysis

contains, perhaps contrary to the intention of most of its adherents, a movement towards personalism. To disregard this would be more than an academic error; it would be quite disastrous. When the psycho-analytic movement is presented in its fundamentals, with all the philosophical embellishment scraped off, it marks a turning-point in the history of psychology and perhaps of science altogether. We rediscover something old—the unity of the human person. Moreover, all that which is of the psychic order is experienced concretely—not through abstracts, not through apparatuses, graphs, and numbers, but with the stark immediacy of poetic insight. Out of the senses Ultimate Sense arises. Out of the dimness of the flesh (*caro*) charity (*caritas*) emerges. This is a pre-eminently human image of the psyche. In the middle of it we find, with overwhelming concreteness, the polarity of love and hate. The human dialogue itself contains a healing principle. And for us who have followed this development, there remains one thing to be added—the world of Grace.